KATHRYN'S
story

KATHRYN'S
story

KATHRYN GREEN

AUTUMN
HOUSE

KATHRYN'S
story

from the publishers

This is, by any standards, a remarkable narrative. The author is 19 and has written her compelling story in a gripping style.

Kathryn Green had ME at a time when the illness was the subject of controversy within the medical profession. Hence, despite what are now regarded as classic symptoms, Kathryn encountered attitudes among the medical fraternity that were less than helpful. Revd Hazel Humphries, the minister of the Methodist congregation of which Kathryn was a member, confirms that at one stage she had to encourage Kathryn to forgive doctors!

Finding an understanding GP was a great help. Dr. N. J. Sparrow has written to us confirming both Kathryn's diagnosis and the fact that, 'in the early part of 1993', she 'made a dramatic recovery'.

Part of the usefulness of *Kathryn's Story* will be, in the view of Glasgow consultant Dr. Martin Clee, to enable readers to understand what ME is and how best to relate to those who suffer from it.

J. C. Walton, PhD, DSc, CChem, FRSC, of the University of St. Andrews, writes: 'In simple, uncomplicated English, Kathryn succeeds in communicating what it is like to have ME. The symptoms are described convincingly and the thoughts, feelings, and reactions of a young girl to this miserable condition come across well. Kathryn is quite frank from the start about the inability of doctors to find anything basically wrong with her blood and other negative tests. Her initial doubtful and hesitant reaction to her wonderful and instant healing gives authenticity to the story. . . .'

'The book gives great insight into the mind of an ME sufferer,' writes Dr. Walton. 'It helps the outsider to know what can be done to help and what not to say and do.' Acknowledging that he 'would fall into the category of the cross-examining doctors whom Kathryn instinctively dislikes', Dr. Walton nevertheless concludes: 'This story is a dramatic one; it is one which will instil faith and trust in God.'

On the bottom line, *Kathryn's Story* is a story of a miracle.

Dr. DAVID MARSHALL, editor

KATHRYN'S
story

CONTENTS

Introduction 9

1 'Kathryn, talk to me!' 11

2 ME gets a grip 17

3 Staying afloat 25

4 Sixteen — and in a wheelchair 31

5 Suspended in time 37

6 Successes — against the odds 45

7 The Jonah rap 51

8 Finding who my friends are 58

9 Disturbing signs 64

10 In the right direction 70

11 SHOUT! — and a healing service 75

12 Only a dream 83

13 A healer, but not a Christian 88

14 Sue's prayer, and miraculous happenings 92

15 Restored 99

16 Through Sue's eyes 104

APPENDIX The minister's testimony 111

Introduction

In September 1990 I was diagnosed as having a disease called Myalgic Encephalomyelitis, often abbreviated to ME.

That, however, may not have been the start of ME. I had suffered from a 'mystery' illness several years before, between the ages of 9 and 12, and had spent a very painful time both physically and emotionally because nobody knew what was wrong with me. I had many tests — which all showed nothing — and went from doctor to doctor.

No doctors could explain why I should be suffering in the way I was, and they began to question the psychological aspect. I saw a child psychologist, was given IQ tests, spent time in hospital under observation and was questioned about everything. Soon every appointment took the form of an interrogation: 'Do you argue with your sister?' . . . 'Do you like school?' . . . Do you have friends?' . . . and so on. It seemed as if all my answers were twisted to fit in with their own theories.

I felt as if everybody thought I was putting it on. The doctors used to tell my parents that I should go to school. I used to cry and not want to go because I felt so ill. I would blame my parents for being cruel — sending me to school when I felt so bad. That caused a lot of pain emotionally for all the family: it felt as though we were being driven apart.

When it seemed we couldn't take any more, I began to improve, very slowly, and recovered enough to go back to school, part time at first and then full time. At last it seemed as if the illness had finally gone forever. I was left feeling a fraud and wondering if I really was strange in the mind, if I had caused my illness and all the trouble myself.

The way I was treated by some doctors in the early days

had undoubtedly had an effect on me which is very hard to shake off. I have found out that many ME sufferers had gone through and are still going through the same kind of experience.

I am writing this book for several reasons: I hope that readers will gain more understanding of ME, both the physical and mental aspects, so that when they come across a sufferer they will understand more of what that person is going through. Writing this down is also good therapy for me, as I went through so many emotions which are now jumbled up inside. Putting them down on paper helps me. Finally, and most importantly, I want this book to be a gift of thanks to God, because of all He has done for me.

CHAPTER 1

'Kathryn, talk to me!'

When I think of 'before ME' I have to think of the years 1988-90. Those were the years of 'remission' or whatever you like to call it. It is hard to remember what I was like before my ME because it was such a long time ago.

After a gradual improvement I took up running. I used to go for a run before breakfast. Although I was never a very sporty person, I came to enjoy PE and most of all I loved walking. As a family we used to do a great deal of walking. My mum, dad, younger sister Alison and I would drive into north Derbyshire then walk miles, taking a picnic with us.

My main hobbies were reading, writing stories, and studying music. I bought myself a portable keyboard at the beginning of 1990 and passed my grade 5 piano exam during the summer of that year.

I belonged to the Girls' Brigade and a choir at church. I had committed my life to Jesus when I was 13, and helped out teaching in the Sunday school when I was 14.

I had always enjoyed school; and at the beginning of this story was in my fourth year at the local comprehensive, working towards GCSEs. I was happy and looking forward to the future. Everything seemed to be going right. I'm glad that I didn't know what actually lay ahead — that my whole life was about to be turned upside down.

During May 1990 I developed a viral infection. I had been feeling run down for a few months beforehand and had had a series of infections, but this infection was the worst of the lot. First my glands swelled, giving me pain in my neck, under my arms and in my groin. I was still going to school, in my fourth year, when I went to see the doctor who decided to do blood tests for glandular fever. Soon after I had had the blood tests I became too ill to attend school.

Besides the swollen glands I developed a fever, aching all over and very tired. The glandular-fever test proved negative, but the doctor said that I had a virus that gave exactly the same symptoms; but it wasn't called glandular fever because it didn't show up on a test. She told me to rest, but when I started to feel better to try, gradually, to do whatever activities I could cope with. It's strange, looking back, because she actually mentioned ME along with her advice, because it's often connected with glandular fever and similar viruses.

I didn't think any more about her ME comment. I had heard of it, but I had no idea what it was or what the symptoms were. I was off school for a month with the viral infection, then went back part time for about three weeks. When I first went back I discovered that I could walk only very slowly and was always tired. I didn't know the reason.

I had been back at school full time for about a week when I took part in work experience. This is a programme that the school organizes every year for fourth-year students, when they go to various firms in the area to gain work experience in whichever job they have an interest. I had helped to arrange my own schedule at two libraries in the area, each with a different system, as I wanted to be a librarian when I left school. I had always loved books and enjoyed organizing things. I spent a very enjoyable week at the libraries and it seemed as if the virus was finally going.

During the last few weeks of school, though, I was far from well. Around that time I took my grade 5 piano exam and had to go to the exam, then be brought straight back because if I had to wait anywhere I felt ill. At lunch times I was always so tired that I used to go into an empty classroom and have a sleep with my head on the desk. I also remember starting to make silly mistakes in my work and spelling words with some of the letters in a confused order. For example, I can remember 'history' becoming 'histyor', and 'the' often became 'teh'. At the time it was a bit of a joke and, anyway, the end of the school year was in sight. I thought with six whole weeks off school I could shake off that illness once and for all and return renewed in health for the last year.

For the first two weeks of the summer holiday I worked. I had one assignment to catch up on because of my time off school, but had been given an extension of the deadline until after the holidays. I also had a few odds and ends of other work to sort out. I liked to get all the work done at the beginning of a holiday, then I could enjoy the rest of the time with nothing hanging over me — a complete break. I was sure that a month of not having to do anything would cure me. We went on holiday to my Aunty Val's near King's Lynn, which is about a two-hour journey. When we arrived I had to go to bed because I was so tired. While there I went off my food. We visited a nearby beach where I kicked a ball around for ten minutes, then lay down and slept for most of the rest of the day. All I can really remember about that holiday was wanting to sleep all the time.

Things did not change when we returned home. I still ate very little. I went shopping with Mum and nearly fainted in the supermarket. That was one of several 'funny turns' that summer. During the hottest nights I was sleeping in thick pyjamas with a winter quilt pulled over my head because I was so cold.

On 1 September, the Sunday before school was due to start again, I went to church. I felt really bad, but I forced myself to go. I could tell that Mum was becoming frustrated with me because I wasn't getting better. She seemed to think that I was just giving in, which wasn't true; I couldn't help it, I felt so ill. While we were in the service there was a coloured blob of light in front of my eye which wouldn't go away. I blinked and blinked but it just grew. When trying to read the hymns I couldn't see the last word on each line because the blob formed a blind spot. We came out of church to go into Sunday school, which was held in another part of the building, and I decided to walk home as I felt too ill to carry on. I found it quite frightening trying to cross the road, because by then half of my right eye was completely blind. I sat quietly in the living-room and very gradually the blind spot went away; but for the rest of that day I had the worst headache I had ever experienced.

Despite all of that, I was determined to go back to school for the first day of the new school year which began the following Tuesday. I had built myself up psychologically to get really stuck in. I was determined not to be brought down by that illness; in fact, I don't think I even thought of it as an illness as such. I did my best to ignore the way I felt. If I ignored it, it would go away. Tuesday wasn't too bad, but Wednesday I felt worse. I ate hardly anything, but still refused to accept defeat.

When I got up on the Thursday morning I seemed to feel a little better than the day before. Dad offered to give me a lift to school, but I decided to walk. 'It'll do me good,' I said. I enjoyed walking and thought that it would clear my head and wake me up a bit.

It was during the second lesson that I began to feel ill. It was French, and we were learning words for different foods. I can remember feeling quite sick and wanting to keep taking deep breaths. At the end of the lesson it took a lot of willpower to get up and walk to the common room for break. I must have looked pale because a friend who was sitting next to me asked if I was all right. I said that I wasn't feeling too good, yet it didn't occur to me to go to the medical room. I couldn't put my finger on what was wrong — I didn't have a pain, so I didn't consider myself ill as such. After break another friend asked, 'Are you all right?'

'No, not really,' I replied.

'What lesson have you got next?'

'Music.'

She knew that music was my favourite lesson. 'Oh, you'll be OK then, won't you?' she said.

'Yes,' I agreed.

I walked to the music block and found that I had to walk slowly. I was feeling bad, yet it still never crossed my mind to seek medical help.

During the lesson I could feel myself going downhill. I couldn't concentrate on what I was doing and didn't dare get out of my chair. By the end of the lesson I wasn't sure how I was going to make it back to the main building. I stood up and pulled my coat on. What felt like a wave of sickness and exhaustion came over me. I put my head down on the desk. In the distance I could hear a piano playing. It faded, and I began to spin down a black hole. . . .

'Kathryn . . . talk to me . . . ' The voice of my music teacher brought me round. 'I feel faint,' I mumbled. He helped me to pull my chair out and put my head between my knees. I banged my head on the desk as I flopped down, still only half with it and not in control of my body. The lesson was over, so most of the pupils had gone. One who was still there went for a drink of water. I could hardly hold the cup to my mouth as my hand and arm wouldn't stop shaking.

After a few minutes the teacher asked if I could try to walk back to the main building and the medical room. I said, 'Yes, I'll try.' We started out, but had walked about ten metres when my legs started to give way and shake underneath me. By the time we got halfway back I could hardly stay on my feet, even with the teacher holding on to me. One of the ladies from the office came to meet us and helped him to hold me up. I just couldn't control my legs and I felt as though I was going to pass out again. Somehow we got to the office area and I was helped onto the first chair we came to. I put my head down because I could feel myself fading out again. We made it to the medical room in two more short stages and I lay down on the bed. Meanwhile, one of the office staff rang my mum to fetch me home. Mum didn't have a car during the day so she had to call on one of the neighbours to give her a lift.

I find it hard to remember getting from the medical room to the car and then from the car to bed. Mum called the doctor, but he didn't want to come out and said to bring me to the surgery later on in the afternoon. The hours between coming home and going to the doctor's went by so fast that I can only think that I must have been unconscious for some of the time. All I can remember is that mum kept talking to me and waking me up. The same friend who had helped us out by giving Mum a lift up to school and bringing us home took us to the surgery. I could still hardly walk and felt awful — I just wanted to go back to bed. The doctor examined me but did not find anything obvious.

CHAPTER 2

ME gets a grip

When I was diagnosed as having ME, both my mum's and my immediate reaction was relief. We had been through so much with doctors and hospitals without a diagnosis and it made sense of what I was suffering then, and my previous problems. I had no real idea what ME was, and felt too ill at that stage to worry about it. I was thinking that maybe I'd have a couple of months off school, which was bad but not disastrous. I'd be able to work at home when things improved a bit. I didn't realize the extent of the change that had happened to my body.

People were very good to me. I had get well cards and flowers. Some of my school friends came to see me and people really showed how much they cared.

Despite all of those good wishes, however, almost all I can remember about that time is darkness. A whole barrage of symptoms was suddenly hitting me. My main memories are of lying or sitting in a darkened room because my eyes and head hurt so much, and sleeping — anywhere. I would walk from my downstairs bedroom to the living-room and go to sleep on the settee. Sometimes, even that kind of short journey was too long for me. I would just curl up on the floor wherever I happened to be when I got tired.

Following is a list of symptoms that I suffered. Some people with ME suffer different symptoms, so this isn't a general checklist for ME. It is just my description of how I felt.

Fatigue. This is not just tiredness as in falling asleep in front of the TV after a hard day at work. It isn't even the kind of tiredness you might get after walking ten miles. It is complete and utter exhaustion to the point of collapse. Every limb is heavy; there is a strange breathlessness as if even your chest muscles haven't got the strength to keep breathing; and a sick feeling that gets worse with any movement. There are days when even turning over in bed makes your heart beat fast, and the sickliness, aching and heaviness never go away. As for energy — what's that? Energy is used up very quickly in performing simple tasks such as getting dressed or eating a meal.

Muscular weakness. Your legs ache continuously. Sometimes the muscles twitch and jump; sometimes they cramp up. Walking may start off quite well, but soon your legs grow heavier until they can no longer straighten under your weight, and every step gets harder and harder. Eventually they shake and crumple; if you still fight it, they become completely useless and out of your control. This isn't something that happens when you try to walk a long way; sometimes it happens all day, as you walk around the house, or when you are tired from being in a room where people are talking. There is nothing you can do about it. The weakness is also in the rest of your body, although it isn't as obvious as in the legs. On bad days it is hard just to lift a spoon up to your mouth to eat; and on a good day holding a pen to write is a real effort. Sitting unsupported on a chair makes your back and stomach muscles hurt.

These are probably the two main symptoms that people with ME get, but there are others which many people do not realize exist.

Disturbed sleep pattern. While I had ME I took antidepressant tablets to help my sleep pattern. Up until then I was quite nocturnal, wanting to sleep all day, then being unable to at night. A typical night without a tablet would be a couple of hours' sleep, maybe. It would be a horrible sleep with confused dreams and I'd wake up feeling so sickly and bad-tempered. Once I had woken up, that would be it, no more sleep for the night. No matter how I tried, it was impossible to get back to sleep; in fact, if anything, I would feel better than I had during the day and want to do things. While it was all very well feeling good in the night and doing things that I felt too ill to do during the day, it was a very anti-social habit and also frustrating. The tablets corrected that routine most of the time, although at some stages I would get out of sync for a while.

Concentration problems. This is one of the really frustrating parts of ME as nobody can observe it. I found with my condition that any kind of reading or writing was impossible to do for longer than ten minutes near the beginning of the illness, and about fifty minutes by the later stages when the problem improved a little. I found that as I read some words they didn't make sense and I'd really have to puzzle over a sentence before I could understand it. The same problem applied when listening to a conversation. Quite often I would have to get my mum to repeat things several times before I could understand them and I would often forget them afterwards. If I was writing I would often spell words wrongly, usually getting letters transposed or even jumbling up words in a sentence.

Headaches and eye problems. At the beginning any kind of light really hurt my eyes. I used to go into my bedroom and put a tiny night light on when it got dark because the light bulb hurt so much. Sometimes I wore dark glasses if I particularly wanted to stay in the main room. Later I bought light reactive glasses which were a big help, particularly in the summer. Sometimes my eyes would blur and other times I saw coloured blobs in front of them. I had very bad headaches at first, although the longer I had ME the less I seemed to suffer from them. At such times I had to lie in a darkened room. I also had pain in one of my eyes and down my face. The doctor gave me migraine tablets which I found helped a lot, although after a bad attack I could still have a very sore eye and head for a few days.

Poor balance. My balance was very poor during my illness. I would often fall over in the house. The doctor tested my balance by telling me to stand up with my eyes shut. She had to catch me!

Feeling cold. During the time I had ME I felt cold. My feet were particularly bad; sometimes they would even go numb and they always looked very white, sometimes almost blue; this pointed to bad circulation. I also had a general coldness and kept on turning up the fire. I got very cold in bed and would take two hot water bottles and wore thick winter pyjamas, even in the summer; and in the winter I often wore a thick cardigan or jumper over the top. I wore woolly bed socks, and over the top of all my clothes was a winter duvet.

Fainting attacks. Those were the most frightening experiences of my ME. I shall go into more detail describing them in a later chapter as the first one I had wasn't until March 1992.

Lack of appetite. Before ME I had a good appetite, typical of a growing teenager. The constant feeling of sickness I had during my illness, and the exhaustion, really put me off eating. I ate to survive and that was about all. I really enjoyed food only occasionally and would often miss meals because I just couldn't face them.

Sensitivity to sound. I tended to develop that when I was particularly tired. Every sound would jangle in my head, making me feel sick and irritable. It would seem as if every noise was magnified and all I could do was find a quiet room to get away. This symptom would often be a warning sign just before I had a fainting attack.

Right from the beginning my GP stressed the importance of trying to do a small amount of exercise, whatever I could cope with, every day. I clung to her advice and every day I went out with Mum. I would aim to get to a particular lamp-post or car on the street, and on a good day I would try to get a bit further than I had been doing. It seemed to help me to cope, making a point to each day, just to improve those few steps. Unfortunately, it wasn't doing my mum much good. I was clinging to her so she took a lot of my weight. When she suggested that I could use a stick to help me, I hated the thought. It seemed important that I didn't give in to having one. Common sense and persuasion finally made me agree, however. Mum borrowed one and I took it with me when I went for my daily walk. It was quite a thin stick made of dark wood, and as I walked I could feel it giving under me. I hated it. It didn't feel safe and I felt like an old woman with it. However, I could then see the point of having a stick and agreed that if the doctor could get me a metal one I would use it. The doctor agreed, and in October I went out for the first time with my new metal stick.

As I walked up the street, leaning heavily on it, I thought that everyone would stare at me and wonder why I needed it. The niggling complex was there that people might think 'she doesn't really need it; she's just using it for effect', even though I knew that without leaning on something I would fall flat on my face. As time went on, though, it was one of the most helpful things I had. I don't know how I could have managed without it. 'Sticky', as I called it, became a close friend.

The days of that first couple of months are quite blurred, and the first very clear event that I remember was the visit to the consultant immunologist.

I sat trembling in the hospital corridor, waiting for my name to be called. I had done things before that had made me nervous — piano exams, concerts — but I felt worse in that hospital corridor than I had ever done before. Because of my previous experiences with doctors I had come to expect interrogation and psychological explanations and, despite Mum's reassurance, I was terrified.

At last we went into a room with an examination bed, a couple of chairs, a desk, and behind that the doctor in his chair. He looked fairly ordinary, but he had the familiar superior look on his face that had been typical of other hospital doctors I had seen the last time I was ill. Before we went in I persuaded myself that I would like him, that since we had a diagnosis things would be different. His first few words made my heart sink.

After I had described my problems, the reason I was there, he asked if I got worried and uptight about going to school. I had heard it so many times before and immediately I felt anger and misery rise up inside me. Having got the 'no' answer, he seemed satisfied and asked me to describe my symptoms. Having heard them he said that I was a typical case of Post-Viral Chronic Fatigue Syndrome. *He didn't believe in ME!* There was no evidence of inflammation around the brain. He then asked me to describe myself — my personality — so I did. Some way through I said that I was a bit of a perfectionist, which I am. I fitted his theory. So-called ME tended to affect perfectionists who couldn't handle the stress that they put themselves under and so became ill and prone to viruses. He had an answer for everything, yet several times he contradicted himself. I couldn't compete with all of it; I felt terrible. Going to the hospital was such an effort anyway; my brain was muddled because of the ME, and I just felt like bursting into tears.

At last he went out of the room to see someone else and I did start to cry then, but when he came back in I managed to hold back the tears, although I felt as if I had no dignity left.

He then made an examination and commented upon the way my pulse was racing. It only served to satisfy his theory of internal stress.

The only good thing that came out of the visit, apart from the fact that it was a consultant's diagnosis, was that he put me on anti-depressant tablets to regulate my sleep pattern. He said that they were non-addictive and seemed to think that if one had the sleep pattern right, recovery would come. He also said that I should have counselling and that, looking at the way we were dressed, he considered £10 a week shouldn't be out of the way. We could have afforded it, but the way he said it was impertinent. 'That's the last time I dress up nicely to go to the hospital!' I thought.

He said that I should forget about school for that year, but we should consider it a failure if I couldn't get back for the next school year. He would see us again in six weeks' time.

At last we made our escape. We had been in there about an hour and it had been an ordeal I would not want to repeat. When we arrived home I just cried and cried. It was probably the most miserable day of my life. It would have been bad enough if I had felt fit, but with my ME it was all too much.

November was a really dark month for me emotionally. I had been hoping to be well enough to get back to school after Christmas; but had come to realize that it was out of the question. I had to come to terms with the fact that it was going to be a long illness, although I still hadn't grasped just how long it would take.

I had to drop all the things that had seemed so important. It looked as if a year of work on nine GCSEs was about to go down the drain and count for nothing. My hopes had been high for As to Cs, but failure, to get nothing, well, it just seemed as if my world was collapsing. I was still very ill. There was some progress, but it was so slight that I had to look back to the beginning of my illness to appreciate it.

Mum and Dad went to Parents' Evening to discuss whether it would be possible to salvage any GCSE grades from the work I had already done. Fortunately, at the time I was doing my GCSEs, some subjects had a good percentage of coursework and I had received good grades on the work I had done in my fourth year. The teachers had looked into things and thought that I could probably get English Language and English Literature with just one more essay; Integrated Humanities, purely with the work I had already done; Music, which I could compose at home; and Maths, if by June I was well enough to take the exams. As June was a long way off, we considered it a possibility. The other subjects were no-go for various reasons. With appeals, then, it was possible that I could get five GCSEs. It was a much brighter prospect than I had thought it might be, although I obviously would rather have got them by doing the full courses like everybody else. The staff at my school were very supportive, and my form teacher, who was also the exam co-ordinator, put in appeals for every subject he could.

Looking back, I can see that there were so many people showing that they cared. I had presents and cards from people whom I would never have thought of. The owners of a butcher's shop in our town, who had known me since I was a little girl, sent me a voucher to get a tape, as listening to music was one of the few things I could do. I had a card signed by my form and they stunned me one Sunday dinner-time when two of them turned up with an enormous bouquet of flowers and a box of chocolates which the form had had a collection to buy. I felt quite choked. All those things helped me to feel that people cared. Those friends who were Christians were praying for me.

The GP whom I was seeing at that time was wonderful, so caring and understanding. She visited me regularly; nothing was too much trouble. She was becoming a friend and I found that I could talk to her in a way that I'd never been able to talk to a doctor before. When I was very down she would help to cheer me up.

I don't know how I would have got through that winter without those people; they kept me going.

After I had given up on school, my attitude towards life had to change. I gave up ambitions for a high-flying career and decided that it was much better to be happy and healthy than anything else.

CHAPTER 3

Staying afloat

Whenever the weather was good enough I would have a walk. It was a joke in our family that Mum would 'walk the dog to the lamp-post' as I always aimed to get to a certain lamp-post. Lamp-posts were the measurement of any improvement. Very slowly there was a little. I gradually got further down the street until one day I managed to turn the corner. The fact that I could actually see some progress, even if it was small, kept me going, but walking was still very difficult.

I would start off reasonably well, just leaning on my stick. The more steps I took the weaker my legs would become. They would start to shake and bend. I tended to walk from my hips and try to keep my legs as straight as I could. If I tried to walk in a more 'normal' way I would fall. Mum got very good at grabbing me, as sometimes I would either lose my balance or my legs would buckle altogether. My legs would also drag and I got breathless from the effort. Often we would have to stop while I sat down on a wall or tree stump to rest.

By the end of the walk I used to be leaning on both Mum and my stick, and would collapse exhausted on the stairs just inside the house.

After a walk I had to rest, often going to sleep. If I pushed myself too hard it could take days or even weeks of starting again and building up to where I had been.

As well as walking, I slowly began to take an interest in life. I would spend hours listening to tapes, and it was at that time that my tape collection started. I began to do jigsaws; proof that my eyes and concentration had improved a bit. I borrowed jigsaws from our neighbours and friends; there was always one in progress on the table. The days were still very long, but at least I was doing something. On good days I could concentrate on a book tape from the library. It had the further advantage of helping the hours pass.

At the beginning of December we were hit by blizzards. We had no electricity for two days and, of course, all the time there was snow and ice on the ground I was imprisoned inside the house. Whenever I see snow and ice now I think about those people who are disabled and can't get out, because I know what the isolation feels like. Even though I had my family for company, I longed for a different face and a change of scenery.

After the blizzards in December, my sister Alison was involved in a musical production at school. She had a small solo singing part at the beginning of the show. I wished that I could go and see her and she wanted me to go, but I knew that there was no way I could sit through a performance. Alison asked the music teacher if I could go and see some of the dress rehearsal the week before, and he agreed. To me it was a big outing. Dad took Mum and me up to school during his dinner hour and we took a taxi back. It was the first time I had been up to school since my collapse and I felt very self-conscious of my stick and clip-on sunglasses to protect my eyes from the light. However, the staff who were around were very friendly and made me feel more comfortable. I enjoyed the half of the show that I saw, but after an hour or so I was ready to leave. My legs had gone completely useless; I was exhausted. But I was glad to have been.

Although going to the rehearsal gave me a lift mentally, unfortunately it didn't last for very long. Christmas came, and I wished that I didn't have to bother. I felt as if I had neither the energy nor the 'goodwill' to celebrate, and became more and more depressed.

Christmas Day 1990 was an event I remember only for the fact that it was my most miserable Christmas ever. I decided to go to the service in the morning and Dad had to bring me back half-way through because I felt so ill. I went into my bedroom and cried, because I should have felt happy but didn't, and the fact that I couldn't do anything didn't help. It was not a happy time.

After Christmas the return visit to the consultant loomed. I got so worked up and worried that my stomach felt like a knot. I would have given anything to get out of going. I counted down the days and hours and kept wishing that it was all over. When I actually got into the room, however, it wasn't anything like the ordeal the last visit had been; and if it had not been for the last time, the consultant might even had seemed likeable. He said that he had to use shock tactics on chronic-fatigue-syndrome patients and that he found those kinds of patients very tiring because he had to work so hard with them. (*He* found it tiring!) We just went along with what he said and played on the fact that I had made some improvement. The consultant knew our GP, whom I had been seeing regularly throughout, and he decided to discharge me so that I would only have to see her. After the worry, the feeling that I had when I left his office was of extreme relief. I didn't have to have any more to do with the hospital and could put the ordeal there behind me.

My 16th birthday was another non-event really, although that was my fault, not anybody else's. It was rather like Christmas because I didn't want to celebrate. I was a year older, so what? It just seemed to show the passing of time, which I hated because it was such a waste. Mum was determined that I should try to enjoy myself so we invited a friend, Rebecca, who had been to see me every week since I had been ill. Rebecca came and did her best for me and I think we had a reasonably happy afternoon, but I honestly don't remember a lot about my birthday, apart from that.

Things began to improve for me psychologically after

my birthday, though. I realized that one of my main frustrations was the fact that time was passing by and I was achieving absolutely nothing. I did jigsaws, but I was getting to the point where I thought, 'What's the use of doing this when I'm only going to pull it apart again afterwards?' I talked to Mum and we decided that I needed a hobby.

Mum went shopping to find a starter kit of something suitable. That was quite difficult because it needed to be something that didn't take too long to do as I could manage only about half-an-hour at a time on a good day. It also needed to be something that didn't tax my eyes and concentration too much.

The first two things she brought were an enamelling kit and colour-beads. First of all I tried the enamelling. The kit had about six pots of coloured enamel, sticks for mixing and using them, pots for mixing, and different metal frames into which I had to pour the enamel. I had to mix the enamels with some hardener and stir them, then pour a small amount into the metal frames provided, on a plastic sheet to stop it from leaking. I could also mix the colours to get different effects. I actually only tried it once because I found that it was too messy and the results took a long time to dry. I didn't take to it. It took too much energy to get ready and then clean and put away.

Next I tried the colour-beads. Using a little hook, I had to place the beads onto a special plastic board with raised points. When I had created the pattern I put greaseproof paper onto the board and beads and ironed it. That melted the beads together and they could then be taken off the board. This hobby was much easier and more relaxing than the enamelling. I started to make sets of coasters and some larger mats on which to stand flowers on a window-sill, or they could be used for other decorative purposes.

At that time a good day would be made up of a walk, making mats, listening to music, sometimes doing part of a jigsaw, with sleeps in between. On a bad day I would hardly be able to get out of bed, but generally I had more good-to-average days than bad ones. They tended to go in runs. I might have a week of good or average days followed by three bad days. Sometimes we could blame the bad days on something extra that I had done on a good day, for example, walking further or not resting quite as much; but I came to the conclusion that good and bad days are just part of the illness, and if you don't make the most of the good days then life doesn't seem worth living.

Boredom struck again and I decided to try out another hobby. I wanted to choose something myself, so we drove to a large toy store on a shopping estate. I managed to walk around with my stick, although it was very tiring. The choice of hobbies was amazing, but it was still difficult to find anything that was suitable. Mum had earlier come up with the idea that I could make things to sell to raise money for ME research. I had liked the idea and was gradually building up a stock of bead mats, but felt I needed to try something else.

In the end I chose a badge-making kit which comprised modelling material and cutters. I quite enjoyed doing this, but unfortunately the results were too weak to sell; so I had to send Mum to the shops again to find some stronger modelling material. She came back with FIMO, which is a bit like Plasticine, in lots of different colours.

You roll the material around in your hands to warm it up and shape it, using the different colours, either mixing or using them as they are, to make your 'creation'. This then has to be baked in the oven for about twenty minutes so that it goes hard. The only tools you need are a knife, something pointed, like a pencil, and some kind of small rolling pin.

First of all I tried making some little ornaments. I was pleased with the results when they had been baked in the oven: a little sheep, a penguin and a bowl of fruit. I decided that I wanted to varnish them, so we got some nail varnish.

What we didn't know was that you should use a special varnish and my ornaments ended up permanently sticky!

Next I started making badges. They turned out better than the ornaments and were easier to make. I did animals: my first one was a teddy bear, then a frog and a rabbit. I really took to my new hobby and slowly began to build up a collection of badges to sell.

Through the winter I made very slow progress, which was only noticeable if I looked back over the six months that I had been ill. Now I know that to make progress in the winter is quite an achievement, but at the time it seemed so slow.

CHAPTER 4

Sixteen – and in a wheelchair

The spring of 1991 was a time of improvement. The improvement was small and slow but definite. I walked a bit further, got out a little more often and, when I was in the house, managed to do more. I still had bad days, but the good days were better than before.

My main activity during that time was the production of badges. I was getting into modelling in a big way, and could see with pride my assorted animal badges improving. Alison wore one to school and came back with a list of orders for her friends. People at church saw Mum's and soon orders were coming in there, too! Word spread and soon I had to buy a notebook in which to keep a list of orders. The good thing about the badges was that they were quick to make, about twenty minutes each, and I could see results before I got too ill to want to go on. As I sold more and more, the money came in and went in a pot for ME research. The butcher's shop had two pig badges with butcher's aprons on, in the window. I made pigs with different football strips, a doctor rabbit for my GP, a dentist rabbit, vicar rabbits, and fulfilled all kinds of other requests. Frogs and pigs were the best sellers, but I made lots of other creatures. I think that within a year I had about fifty different designs.

As always, I needed a target, a special day to aim for and look forward to. That took the form of a coffee morning at church to raise money for ME research. We booked a date and I decided to have a craft stall where I could also sell bead mats. I began to try different ideas such as fridge magnets and ornaments, although my main output was still badges.

The fact that I had an aim, making money for research

n activity that I enjoyed and could manage to do, apart on bad days, was very good for me mentally.

Gradually my stocks built up and the preparations began. We found some information from the ME association. This, along with articles from their magazines, was displayed on a pin board. Posters were placed in various locations in the community. Refreshments were bought. At last the big day came.

I knew that I wouldn't be able to go across to the church for the whole time. It would be on from 10am until noon, and two hours would tire me out. I decided to go and help with the setting up, then go home until about 11am, returning for as long as I could cope. When I arrived at about eleven o'clock it was quite busy. I sat behind my craft stall with Rebecca who had been covering for me while I couldn't be there. Quite a lot of my badges and fridge magnets had been sold, and on our stall the money was starting to mount up. Next to us was the cake stall which was doing amazingly good business. At the beginning there had been a tableful and through the morning not only had people bought cakes, but many had donated even more! As fast as one cake was sold, another took its place.

There were a lot of faces that I didn't know. We had a 'name the teddy competition', which two members of the junior church had wanted to organize, and a 'guess the weight of the cake'. I was pleased to see people browsing through the ME magazines we had put out and reading the articles on the boards. I felt that raising awareness of ME was just as important as raising money.

During the hour or so that I was there, I met Helen for the first time. Helen, who is a couple of years younger than I, is also an ME sufferer. Her mum is a teacher at my old school and that was how we first got in touch. We had written to each other a few times and obviously had things in common apart from the fact that we both had ME. The coffee morning was a good chance for us to meet. Afterwards,

Mum, Dad and Alison all commented on the fact that Helen walked in a similar way to me. We called it 'the ME walk' and later could see it in other ME sufferers. Helen and I hit it off straight away and have remained good friends ever since. It was really good to be able to put a face to the name, as it is so much easier to write to someone whom you have met. After that we visited each other when our ME was at a reasonable level and continued to write.

I managed to stay until the end of the coffee morning, and when the money had been counted we had £200! That was excellent for two hours; we never expected to raise so much. A friend had been doing a sponsored wool spin during the morning and her amount, along with what I had got at home from selling badges, and the proceeds from the coffee morning, came to £310. It was all profit. Expenses for modelling materials and other things had been taken out of my float at home. I was exhausted, but felt such a sense of achievement that it was all worthwhile.

As the weather began to improve during the spring, I began to get restless and bored with being indoors so much. The most that I could manage on a good day was to walk around a certain block of houses once, and that brought me to the verge of exhaustion every time. It was hardly enjoyable and I never got out of the same area. The only chance to get away from home was a drive in the car at the weekend, and even when I got away I could still walk only a very short distance or watch the countryside go by from inside the car.

Mum had suggested the idea of a wheelchair before, but I had fought it. I couldn't stand the thought of being pushed around and stared at. I thought that to have a wheelchair would be giving in and becoming 'disabled', which I just couldn't accept.

Near the beginning of my illness a wheelchair wouldn't have been of much use to me. Just the motion and bumping would have tired me too much. But with my improvement my interest in life was growing.

At Easter our church often has a family walk and picnic. That year they were going to Sherwood Forest. Some of the young people in the church had suggested that I could borrow a wheelchair and that they would be happy to take it in turns to push. I had said, 'No thank you.'

However, the longing to go out continued, and I so much wanted to be among my friends in the church and to go out and do something normal. Eventually, at the last minute, with encouragement from my family, I decided to go. We had to make arrangements quickly to borrow a wheelchair from a lady a couple of streets away who mainly used an electric one and had as a spare an ordinary push version. She had said on previous occasions that we were welcome to use it, and she arranged for me to borrow a muff from somebody else to keep me warm. I went in one car and the wheelchair in another. Everything had been very well organized.

I think part of the reason I changed my mind was the fact that the people at church made me feel so welcome; and I knew they would accept me in a wheelchair and not treat me any differently from anybody else. The other thing was that Sherwood Forest was a safe distance from home. The chances of meeting anybody I knew, apart from the church group, were low. I particularly dreaded meeting school friends. The thought of being pushed around where everybody could see me was still out of the question. That outing would just be a one-off.

The night before, I worried that it would rain and all the preparation would be for nothing. I knew that I would be disappointed if I couldn't go. Outings were rare; and what most people took for granted was a major treat for me.

Fortunately it was fine, a bit dull, but fine. Despite my worries about feeling conspicuous, it was a really good day out. Everybody took it in turns to push me; and rather than feeling like a burden, I found it was good fun. I ended up in the bushes more than once! It felt good to be out in the countryside among friends who just accepted me as I was. I was exhausted by the time we got home; but I had coped very well, better than I had expected.

A couple of weeks passed, then one particularly good spring day I just had to get out. Mum went round to borrow the wheelchair and that evening we went out. I was wrapped up well as it was still chilly, and Mum pushed me. We went only a fairly short way, but it was further than I'd been for such a long time, apart from at Easter, and instead of feeling chained to the wheelchair, I felt released and free. Of course, it was strange and I felt very self-conscious and didn't want to meet anybody I knew, but I realized that so much could be opened up to me through the wheelchair.

I decided that it was time to stop relying on the friend and get my own.

On my next visit to the doctor I asked her about getting one. She agreed that it would be helpful and applied for us. Soon, a brand-new, red-and-grey wheelchair was delivered to the door. It was slightly smaller than the one I had been borrowing, and I found it more comfortable, as I didn't bump around in it so much.

Having the wheelchair was the best decision I could have made. Looking back, I don't know how I could have coped through my illness without it. Although I was still very limited because of my low energy level and general 'ill' feeling, I was no longer limited by my useless legs. Whenever the weather was fine and I felt well enough, Mum would take me out. I still continued to have a walk each day, trying to improve the distance all the time, but the wheelchair made the incredibly slow progress much more bearable.

My walking was improving slightly. My concentration, though, was still very poor. We had talked with the school and come to the decision that I would be entered for five

GCSEs: English Language, English Literature, Integrated Humanities, Maths and Music. Both of the English subjects were 100 per cent coursework. I had worked hard and earned some good marks during my fourth year; and the teachers felt that if I could have one more essay on a piece of drama for my literature folder there would be enough to enter me with an appeal. As I found reading very difficult, I borrowed a video from school of Shakespeare's *Romeo and Juliet*. When I had watched it a few times one of the English staff came to my house to talk me through the essay question and help me plan my essay. Slowly I began to write. It really was slow, too, as I could manage only a paragraph a day. I had always enjoyed English before my illness and even from a young age used to love to write, yet at that time it was just like trying to think through a fog. If I read anything I had to read each sentence several times before taking it in and understanding the words. I found myself constructing sentences with words in the wrong order and making spelling mistakes in the simplest of words. It was very frustrating, but sentence by sentence, paragraph by paragraph, the essay was written.

I didn't need to do any more work towards my Integrated Humanities folder which was also 100 per cent coursework. We entered my fourth-year work with an appeal.

I had also completed enough Maths coursework, but part of the Maths GCSE was a written exam. I decided to have a go.

The Music GCSE also consisted of part coursework and part exam. I decided to have a go at that exam, too. The coursework requirement was recorded compositions and performances which I could work on at home, then the music teacher would come and record it with the school equipment.

The weather improved; the winter was behind, and the summer was ahead. I felt optimistic about my future and felt sure I was improving and that from then on there would be a gradual improvement leading to my recovery.

CHAPTER 5

Suspended in time

During my illness I had to have things to hold on to, to keep me going and keep me sane. Obviously, too, there was always the hope that I would get better, as many people do to a reasonable level, or even recover completely. Although that hope was there, it was often very dim and it seemed that recovery was a long way away for most of the time. I had to have other short-term things to keep my spirits up and give me a reason to go on living. It meant accepting my illness and doing what I could within its limitations.

There was always back-up from friends and family, from the church and from the community, and when I tried to do things, they all encouraged me. A few of our closest friends would visit regularly, but even then I could often cope only with short visits. I spent a lot of time on my own, apart from my family always being there, and psychologically it was important that I achieved something good out of what was a bad time.

One of the main things that helped me was playing and listening to music. Even during the early days of my illness I was able to listen to some music. I hardly had any tapes before that time; now I have boxes full of them! It was some time during the winter of 1990/91 when I discovered just how many Christian tapes are available, and how many different styles there were.

One day when Mum was going into the city shopping, I asked her to try to find me a tape in the Christian bookshop. 'Something fairly modern', I said, as I didn't want just a traditional hymn-singing tape. When Mum came back she had three tapes which had been much cheaper than usual because they were 'samplers'. One was a mixture of praise and worship songs; one was a group, and the other was a mixture of contemporary music. The one I liked most, and which came as the greatest surprise was the contemporary mixture. I had soon picked out artists that I liked on the tape and sent Mum back to the shop to find their recordings. Some we had to order; others were on the shelves. Since then my collection of Christian tapes has grown and grown. I often find that they inspire or comfort me. Because of my illness, I had great difficulty in reading the Bible or coping with a church service. The Christian music tapes were the only spiritual nourishment I was getting, and they helped tremendously. Often the words of a song would hit me as if God was talking directly to me. Sometimes they were words of encouragement, or they described exactly how I felt and offered hope. Sometimes they would be songs of commitment with which I could identify as I prayed.

The words of one song on a tape bought in the summer of 1991 were especially relevant. They hit me so hard because they were talking about waiting on the Lord for His will and that He could hear me, even though I was going through a bad time. During that summer I was managing to read the Bible a little bit, and the strange thing was that only about a week after the song affected me, I came to read the passage of the Bible on which it was based:

'He strengthens those who are weak and tired. Even those who are young grow weak; young men can fall exhausted. But those who trust in the Lord for help will find their strength renewed. They will rise on wings like eagles; they will run and not get weary; they will walk and not grow weak.' Isaiah 40:29-31, TEV.

That seemed to give me a message of hope to which I clung. I was young, and weak, and tired, and prayed that one day my strength would be renewed. The thought of being able to walk and run again, and of not feeling weary or weak made me cry because I longed for it so much. The image of an eagle flying high above the earth helped me remember that God was there and that He would help me get through my problems. I felt as if those words were a personal promise to me from God.

As well as listening to music, I found playing music very helpful. Although I stopped having piano lessons, I still played whenever I felt well enough. I can remember lying in bed with a tune going around my head and having to get up and try it out on the piano. That was a matter of weeks after my collapse and it marked the start of my first composition of my illness, which I later put towards my GCSE music coursework. Although it was never a song with words, there were thoughts going around my head. I was still getting used to the idea that I had a bad illness and knew that it would change the course of my life. Writing that piece of music helped me express my emotions. In the early stages of my illness I found it hard to communicate because my concentration was bad and I found speech slow and difficult. Amazingly, despite my concentration problem, I could compose and remember music, although playing would tire me quickly and make my arms hurt.

During my illness I wrote about ten compositions of instrumental music and the same number of songs. Those were the first songs I had ever written as I had never before known how to write lyrics. The words of those songs expressed my feelings as I thought both of my life and the world around me.

Most of my compositions were worked on a keyboard. Over the two-and-a-half years I gradually acquired more equipment. Since I couldn't go out anywhere and didn't buy many clothes, I saved my money and spent it on music equipment. Mum and Dad encouraged me as they knew how much pleasure I got out of it. Without my music I don't know how I would have coped.

I found that song-writing was one of the best ways of getting frustration out of my system. Sometimes I would compose songs which I would never actually put down on paper. One song I did write down and produce properly on my keyboard was 'Suspended in time'. I wrote it at a time when I was very down, because whenever I seemed to be getting a bit better I would relapse and have to start all over again.

Suspended in Time

It seems I spent too much time
Chasing after dreams,
Just get there in time
To find that it's not real.
How many times must I say
What's the point of it all anyway?
My life has been on pause since that day.

Suspended in time
Suspended in time
I'm spending my life
Suspended in time.

All my plans and hopes
Went flying out the door:
Broken pieces scattered
All over the floor.
Everything's gone down the drain
When will I get through this pain
To pick up the pieces of my life again?

Suspended in time
Suspended in time
I'm spending my life
Suspended in time

'Just take every day'
Is so easy to say
But advice is never easy to take.

Suspended in time
Suspended in time
I'm spending my life
Suspended in time
Suspended in time.

My songs weren't usually as negative as that, though. The next song was called 'Jesus' love never ends'. I must have been feeling better by then! 'Suspended in time' is the only song I wrote about my negative feelings because of ME, but it was good, because it helped me to express myself.

During my illness I tried out lots of different crafts and discovered talents for things that I would never have dreamt of doing unless I had been ill. They started with the peg mats and badges and progressed to cross-stitch later on, when my eyes and concentration were quite a lot better in comparison. As well as filling in the time, I could use the hobbies as a means of raising money. That was also very important to me since I felt a sense of achievement from seeing the money mount up, and I felt as if I was helping towards research which hopefully would ultimately find a cure. I knew that it would take a long time, but I thought that at least I might be helping somebody else in the future with ME. I could see something good and positive coming out of what would otherwise be a complete waste of time as far as I was concerned.

Belonging to the ME Association helped, as they gave out information about research that was happening and the results of various programmes. It was good psychologically to see that something was being done and to feel a part of it.

Walking was another target which helped me through the first year. I would aim to walk those few steps further every few days and, although there were a lot of ups and downs, I could measure how I was getting on physically by the distance I could walk, but I had to be careful not to push myself beyond my limits.

Although concentration was very difficult, I got some sense of achievement out of trying to do a small amount of work. During the first part of my illness, for about a year, that was almost impossible, but later on I found that my concentration improved quite a bit and I was able to work for up to an hour on a good day. Although my efforts to study often came to nothing insofar as gaining an extra qualification was concerned, it was enjoyable and interesting.

When you have a long-term illness it is very easy to feel down and depressed because there is nothing to look forward to. Having little events or outings is very important so that there is something in the future to give some kind of structure to life. It might be an outing to a few shops or a park, a holiday or fund-raising activity. Holidays were very important to me. They meant that I could get away from the house which would at times feel like a prison when I couldn't get out. When I went away it needed to be for about a week if a long journey was involved as it took me a couple of days to recover. Also it was sometimes good to go on my own to relatives, as it meant that I got away from Mum, Dad and Alison, and they had a break from me when they could do whatever they wanted.

Going out on a day-to-day basis was also important. The wheelchair was the biggest help there; without it I would have hardly ever been further than the bottom of the street, and I would have been confined to the house even more. Mum would push me around the streets of our local area. Sometimes we went on short shopping trips; occasionally we went to friends' houses, and often we just went around for the pleasure of being out.

All of those activities and outings helped me in the best way to cope with ME. I had to carry them out in moderation and, of course, there were bad days when I could do nothing. But I found that if I could get some enjoyment out of the good days, then it made the others more bearable.

I have already talked of how people were so good, rallying around me while I was ill, and that helped a lot, though not everything people said and did was positive. I know that a lot of the time the hurtful things that were said were completely unintentional; but it is important to explain why some things upset me so that other people can learn to avoid making the same mistakes.

One attitude which used to upset and annoy me was when people seemed to think that if I really wanted to do something I could 'rise above' my illness and do it. It was true that if I really wanted to do something I might push myself a bit harder, but in the end my illness would always have the final say. The trouble was that people would see me only when I managed to get out and do something; they didn't know about the hundreds of times I wanted to go out and couldn't. It is so frustrating when you want to do something and can't, and it's upsetting when you do manage to do something and it's put down to the fact that it's something you really wanted to do so you could 'rise above it'. 'Mind over matter' does not always work.

Often people seem to think they know best, even though they have never had the illness and don't have to live with it. The advice they give may be with the best intentions, but so often they fail to grasp the fact that nobody enjoys sitting at home doing nothing and that if someone with ME pushes herself even that tiny bit beyond her limit, it can make her worse for days, and in the end she is the one who has to suffer. Sometimes people think that the person who is ill should be making more effort to do certain things. I found that those were usually things I would have really liked to have done but couldn't. Obviously, if somebody is trying to persuade you to do something you really want to do, yet you know that if you do it you will be too ill afterwards, it is very frustrating.

There are always tactless questions to avoid with ME, as with any other long-term illness. Questions such as the following made me cross: 'When do you think you will be able to . . . ?' 'How long do you think it will be before you are better?' 'What do you want to do career-wise?' Or 'Are you better now?' The last question comes because you might look slightly better or are having a good day.

I think that most of these problems come from a lack of understanding about the disease, particularly with people who have never been very ill. Hopefully, as awareness of ME is raised generally, people will come to understand how to cope with sufferers in a more sensible way.

CHAPTER 6

Successes – against the odds

The exams loomed as spring turned into summer. I had planned to take Music, which was made up of one short practical exam and a longer written exam, and Maths which was about three papers. The Music came first, so I tried to put the Maths to the back of my mind, but I couldn't help worrying. Maths was hard when my concentration was at its best. With my brain so muddled I couldn't see how I was going to cope.

The practical Music exam came first. It was a short exam, lasting about twenty minutes, which involved improvisation and aural tests. Although it was tiring I didn't find it too bad. I knew that the written exam was going to be the real test as it consisted of two papers of forty minutes each. Everybody finds exams difficult, but I found that the most frustrating thing was knowing what I wanted to write, yet getting the answers onto paper was so difficult. As the time went on it got worse, then my brain began to get muddled as well, until I knew that I had to stop. That happened about half-way through the second paper. When I stopped, I realized how awful I felt. My muscles were heavy and useless; my head and eyes ached and I felt sick with exhaustion. At last everybody had finished and I could go home. Mum was waiting in a room next door and with the help of the music teacher she almost had to carry me to the car. For a couple of weeks after the exam I was so ill that we realized there was no way I could cope with the Maths exams. It would be foolish to risk my health. Physically and mentally I knew that I just couldn't manage it. I had to accept that I would have to let the Maths go. The staff at school were more hopeful, though. They put in a special appeal to see if I could be assessed just on the coursework done in my fourth year. My form teacher was the exam co-ordinator for my school that year and was determined to do whatever he could. So I waited and hoped for the next few months, wondering whether I could possibly get five GCSEs and, if so, what grades.

In the meantime I did my best to enjoy a good summer. Fortunately, the effects of the music exams were only short term and I picked up again reasonably quickly, within a month or so. I spent a lot of time lying on the sunbed outside with my head in the shade and my body and legs in the sun. The warmth really seemed to help my legs. From when I first started sunning my legs, my walking improved at a much quicker rate. On my best days I could even walk some of the way without my stick! At my peak I walked about half a mile using the stick. My concentration was still quite poor, however, and lack of stamina meant that outings were confined to about half a day, and, of course, there were always the bad days when even turning over in bed was too much effort.

Although my walking had improved, I couldn't walk in a normal way. I had to keep my legs stiff and swing my hips rather than bend my knees. My right leg would often drag when I was starting to get tired and I would lose my balance and veer off in the wrong direction. When I pushed myself to the limit both legs would drag; my knees would sag and my legs shake with weakness. I often had to sit down on whatever happened to be available. I could manage a maximum of one long walk or two short ones a day. However, overall, I was very pleased with my progress.

It was at about that time that Mum told me she felt she should resign from the Sunday School, or Junior Church as we call it. She said she felt as if she was being told by God to leave. My immediate reaction was, 'Oh, no, if you leave, it really will go downhill!' At the time, Junior Church was struggling a little, nothing drastic, but neither was it really flourishing. The Junior Church consisted of Sue and

Eddie, the superintendents, Mum, who played the piano and took the 7-8-year-olds, and Heather and David, who taught the 11-12s and the teenagers. I used to teach in the Junior Church, before my illness, sharing Mum's class. On a good Sunday there would be about twelve children. We would sing for a while with little enthusiasm, then split into age groups and each teacher had a book to base his or her lesson on. It was then up to the teacher until the end when we got back together, and had another song and a prayer. There was nothing wrong with all of that; it was just not very lively and a bit old-fashioned.

When Mum said she was leaving I was surprised and couldn't help wondering why God would want her to go! What would they do for music? Besides that, they would need another teacher.

I don't think the idea came to me until a couple of months later: the idea that I could go in and play my keyboard! I can't even remember where the idea came from, but as soon as I thought of it I liked it. I bought myself a *Junior Praise* and went to work, arranging the various songs that the children and young people knew. It was good fun; with the pre-set backings on my keyboard I could turn the songs and choruses from just a tune on a piano to a pop arrangement, or any other style. I was thoroughly enjoying doing something useful with my music and just hoped I would be able to cope with the forty-five minutes of Junior Church.

While I was working on the songs, I also bought an amplifier which was really necessary to get enough volume to lead the children singing. It brought out the bass and drums and made the keyboard sound much better. Through the summer I prepared, aiming to be ready for September.

In the meantime, we had a holiday in the Cotswolds. The car was packed with the obvious things, cases and bags, but also with my wheelchair and muff. We literally had to pack things around us once we were in!

It was good to get away from the house into the lovely countryside and little villages; but I also remember it being a frustrating holiday because I could manage only half-day outings, which restricted the whole family. Overall, though, it was a good holiday. The weather was fine; the accommodation was good and it was a change of surroundings for all of us. Having spent the best part of a year within the same square mile I was relieved to get out. Staying in the same small area can be quite claustrophobic, especially if one has little choice in the matter.

After the holiday it was back to normal and the next concern was my GCSE results. I had decided to have them posted to me rather than going up to school, as it necessitated Mum's taking me up in my wheelchair. It meant that I received them a day after my friends had theirs. When the envelope came I hardly dare open it. I knew that those at school had done their best with the appeals, but in the last analysis the decision was up to the examination board. I opened the envelope and pulled out the computer print-outs. On one it said, 'English Language: A, English Literature: A, Humanities: A, Music: A'; and on the other, 'Mathematics: B.' The feeling that swept over me was a mixture of joy and relief. The thought that all my fourth-year work could have been for nothing had been awful. At least I had received something to build on in the future, and I was so pleased with the grades. Having got my grades, I then dared to ring some of my friends and found out that they had done really well, too. That night I rang round the relatives to tell them the good news and everybody was pleased for me.

Looking back, I see that that summer was a high point in my illness, when I was at my best, physically and at my most positive mentally. The GCSE success encouraged me to look forward and to think about completing two more GCSEs, History and French. I had not been able to get History on an appeal because I lacked sufficient coursework and it involved taking an exam. The French consisted of a hundred per cent examination work, so there was no other way I could be assessed. My form teacher, who also taught me History, had already offered his help in the event of my wanting to take further studies, so I decided that after the holiday I would contact him. I felt confident that I would be able to cope with a few lessons and the work for two subjects, and looked forward to the following September.

Although I was feeling better than I had for a long time, I still couldn't get out and meet people very often, and suffered from loneliness. I decided to buy a pet to keep me company in my room. I wasn't really into dogs or cats, but I liked birds, so I bought myself a budgie. Right from the first day he was tame. Straightaway he would sit on my hand and eat from it. I decided to call him 'Sparky' because he had such a bright and friendly personality. Sparky is bright green and yellow and when he was young had a tuft of feathers on his head that stuck up. I let him come out of his cage every day and tamed him. At first he was very naughty and when it was time for him to go into his cage I had a job getting him back. Gradually, though, he calmed down. Although Sparky has never been able to talk, he imitates the percussion noises on my keyboard and barks like the dog a couple of doors away. He was company during my illness. Instead of talking to myself, I would talk to Sparky!

At the end of August I bought myself a new keyboard. It wasn't something I had planned to do in the near future, yet looking back, I think it was one of the best things I did as it opened the way for me to extend my horizons.

It was one Saturday when Mum was taking me out in my wheelchair. As we were passing an electrical goods store we decided to go in to have a look around. On display were some keyboards which were switched on so that people could try them out. Sitting in my wheelchair I found one that was just on my level and began to experiment. It was the next model up from the keyboard I already had and not much more than mine had been in price, yet it was so much better. The sounds were of a better quality; the styles were modern, and it had a few extra features, including a simple eight-track sequencer. The keyboard that I owned had a song memory, but I could easily exhaust the space in it and I could have only five notes playing at a time. I fell in love with that keyboard and wanted it. Mum had to drag me away because she could see a salesman about to pounce! On the way home I couldn't stop talking about it and tried to persuade Mum to let me take some money out of my savings to buy it. She didn't know much about keyboards so I had to explain why it was so good. Finally, she said that it was my money and if I felt sure it was what I wanted then I could buy it.

Next I had to talk Dad round. That wasn't as hard as I thought it might be. He said he knew nothing about music, but if I wanted it, then I should go for it. That same day I took Dad to the shop to see the keyboard (or at least persuaded him and he pushed me!). Mum came with us. We had a demonstration from the salesman and he agreed to reserve a keyboard for me until the following Monday when I could draw some money out of my account to buy it.

We collected the keyboard and set it up in my bedroom. It was like a dream. When I really get into my music, especially something new, I tend to go into a daze and none of my family can get through to me. That was what happened, and all I can remember about the next week or so was playing the new keyboard and finding out what it could do.

I kept the old keyboard because I had arranged a great deal of the Junior Church music on it. I knew that it wasn't worth a lot to sell as the new models were improving all the time, and mine was a few years old, so for a while I had two keyboards.

CHAPTER 7

The Jonah Rap

September came and I was optimistic; it seemed that I had plenty to look forward to. I was starting back at school for a few lessons a week and intending to start playing the keyboard in Junior Church.

School began and I went to see about going in. I had a lift to school and walked into the office building on my own. I had written to tell my teacher that I was coming in at break-time, and he came down to see me. I was hoping to do three lessons each of GCSE French and History a week, but the first thing we discovered was that the lessons clashed. It meant that I would have to cut it down to three lessons split between the two subjects. Looking back, I believe I would never have coped with six lessons a week anyway. There was one single and a double, which meant that I would be going in two mornings a week.

Back at home, Mum rang a local taxi firm and made a regular arrangement to take me to and from school for the lessons.

It soon became obvious that I wasn't coping with the double lessons. After only two weeks my ME had plummeted, and that was after leaving the double period early. I just couldn't do it. I had over-estimated my progress. We came to a new arrangement. Two days a week I went into school for a single History lesson, and another day a teacher gave me an hour of private tuition in French at home. That worked, and although the lessons, and the journeys, exhausted me, I enjoyed them.

When I first went into the History class it wasn't easy because I didn't have any friends there; they were now new fifth formers. After a few lessons I made a friend and began to fit in better. At the end of the lesson my teacher would walk down to the taxi with me. I was grateful for that. By then I would be very tired and often not too stable.

At home I enjoyed having a tutor and got on with her really well. It was good having a regular visitor as well as having the satisfaction of doing some work. Going to school and having a tutor were good for me socially. I got out of the house regularly on my own and met different people.

The second way that I was getting back into life was by going in to Junior Church to play. The first week I was quite nervous. I had arranged quite a few well-known songs in a new way. Only the family had heard what I was doing, so when I started on the first song, the surprise on everyone's face was obvious. They had been used to the piano, so when the drums and full backing came in it was quite a shock, but I think it was a pleasant shock. Usually it was a struggle to get the kids to sing with any enthusiasm, but that morning they didn't want to stop and were disappointed when it was time for the lesson. Sue was obviously enjoying the music, too, and was excited about it. She promised the Junior Church that the next week we would have a session of just singing with the keyboard. Although it was very tiring, both physically and mentally, I had really enjoyed playing and it gave me a buzz to see the young people so enthusiastic and excited. In the past they had sometimes just sat and stared into space like zombies.

During the Sundays that followed, Junior Church changed dramatically. Instead of our going into small separate groups as we had done in the past, we did more as a whole group. We explored things we had never done before, such as dance and mime. New enthusiasm and ideas seemed to be injected into both the leaders and young people. One of the leaders had a video camera which he brought in and filmed the youngsters doing some drama. We grew in number, with an average of seventeen a week.

I can't remember exactly how the Jonah Rap came about. We were doing the story of Jonah in Junior Church and I can't remember whether Sue asked me to try to write a rap or if I just wrote it on the spur of the moment. All I can remember is that I woke up one morning, read the story of Jonah in the Bible and wrote a rap. By mid-morning I had a rhythm and backing going on my keyboard and that was it. When Alison came home from school I played it and taught it to her, with the idea that we could demonstrate it in Junior Church the next week. I checked with Sue and it was all right, so we were all set.

Again I was nervous, especially because it was something I had written. Children don't wrap it up: they won't pretend to like something if they don't. That Sunday morning I played the Jonah Rap over and over again because they liked it so much. The Rap had a few lines that were like a chorus. They picked them up quickly and we soon had the Jonah Rap with the chorus and then the Jonah Rap with dance! It was all so spontaneous!

David, the leader with the video camera, came up with the idea of doing a pop video for the Jonah Rap. It was a project which took us a couple of months altogether. If you watch a pop video you will see that it is often made up of a lot of very short pieces of film put together. David drew up a second-by-second plan for the video by timing various parts of the rap. We recorded the soundtrack in one week. Alison did the main rap and the rest of the Junior Church joined in with the chorus. For a couple of weeks we filmed the Junior Church as they did a mixture of 'rapping', dancing, and miming actions to do with the story. David then took it all home and did an excellent and time-consuming job of fitting all the snippets together, while making sure that they synchronized with the song. We were very proud of the result. The final stage was playing the Jonah Rap pop video in church so that the congregation could see what we had been doing. It was an all-round success. We had all enjoyed doing it, and those who watched appreciated it. We thought that it must be quite original and revolutionary to have a pop video shown in church!

While all that was going on, though, my health was getting worse. During the day I continued to make Christmas badges, which were very popular. I decided that the money I raised from these would go to the piano fund at church, to raise money for a new piano to be permanently placed in church. By then I was getting quite fast at making badges, and between September and Christmas I made about 200 which sold for 50p each. The days were very dark and long. The bad weather meant I couldn't go out very much and it was lonely. At least the badges gave me something to do. I was still managing school but it seemed that as the weather deteriorated so did my ME. Everything got harder and harder. I was worse after lessons. During the summer my hopes and expectations had risen. I had been sure that I was getting better, but the winter months brought on a worsening of my condition and the following summer seemed a long way away. Depression began to set in.

As I got more and more down, I felt further and further away from God. I thought, 'If God loves me, how can He leave me alone like this? Why do I have to be ill anyway? It isn't fair!' My prayers were mainly restricted to, 'Oh, please, don't let my legs go now,' when I was struggling to get down to the taxi at school in front of the fourth years at break time, or desperation prayers when I felt I couldn't cope any more. Yes, I did consider suicide. There was a jar full of anti-depressant tablets which the doctor had given me to regulate my sleep pattern. I could easily have taken them before I went to bed and nobody would have known until morning. I knew, though, that if I did it, I would have to do it properly. There was no way I wanted to wake up in a hospital bed and have to face psychiatrists saying, 'We told you so. It's all in the mind!'

Although sometimes it seemed as if going to sleep and never waking up again would be the best thing, I never had the guts nor the conviction to do anything. Even at my lowest points I still believed that God existed, although I might question what He was doing. I think it was that, and the glimmer of hope — the fact that you can get better from ME — that helped me through the lowest hours, plus love for my family. I didn't want to let them down.

As I struggled around the small block of houses on my stick with Mum, I tried to explain something of how I felt. Even if you have a short illness and are stuck in the house, you get tired of the same four walls, and that was how I felt. The house was like a little box that I was stuck inside; and even when I got out, it was only around the same few streets. The winter seemed to stretch ahead and I felt as if there was no hope of my getting any better until the summer. In fact I could feel myself getting worse and worse. Then the more depressed I got, the less I felt like exerting myself. Everything seemed pointless and the less I did, the more depressed I became.

Mum knew that we had to break the cycle somehow, so she came up with the idea of our going to my Aunty Mary's on the train for a week as a break. That appealed to me, so we arranged it with my Aunty and Uncle for about the second week in November.

It was a three-hour train journey. I slept for most of it, yet by the time we arrived I was exhausted and had to struggle to get into the car, and then into the house. The train journey didn't affect me as much as a car journey would have done, though, and through the week at Aunty Mary's my ME was about normal.

During the week my spirits rose. It was the change of house and the change of area. I could walk around a different block of houses. My cousin Joanne, who is two years older than I, took us all out in the car, and so we saw a different district too. Normally at home during the week we couldn't go far because Dad had the car for work and I couldn't travel on buses. It was too difficult getting on and off, and I needed to have the wheelchair to get around, anyway. Aunty Mary had borrowed a wheelchair, which was old and falling apart, but it was all right just for the week, although by the end it had about had it!

I enjoyed seeing my cousin and spending time with someone of a similar age. I began to feel more positive about the future, too. In the past hobbies had given me a reason to get up in the morning, so I took them up again. Although at the time I was still making Christmas badges, I began to plan what I would do next. I decided to make fridge magnets, ornaments, key-rings, ear-rings and buttons; lots of ideas came into my head for new designs. We planned another coffee morning for the following spring, and I also had the idea of having a stand at my school's craft fair in a year's time to raise money. We went to a craft fair while I was there, and looking at prices I realized that what I was charging was very reasonable yet I was making a good profit for charity, too. The idea seemed realistic.

When we came home the ideas were still there, but my spirits seemed to sink again. Maybe not as bad as before, but heading that way.

Only a couple of weeks after I came back from Aunty Mary's I got an unexpected chance to go away again. Each year a party from our church and two neighbouring churches go to Willersley, not far from Matlock, Derbyshire, which is a Methodist Guild Holiday Home. My family had never been before and hadn't booked for that year, either, but somebody dropped out at the last minute and so a place had become available. Knowing that I had been low, and that a complete break from the family might help, our minister, Hazel, came to offer me the place. It was only for a weekend so I decided that I should be able to cope and agreed to go.

I don't know what it was about that weekend at Willersley, but it helped me a lot. There were so many caring people at our church and they, particularly Hazel, looked after me well. Although I couldn't join in with everything, there was always somebody around to chat to, and I enjoyed just sitting and relaxing somewhere different. Hazel even brought me a new craft to try. It was making flowers from wire and a kind of lacquer-paint. You made loops with the wire and dipped them into the paint which formed a film over the loops, making petals and leaves. You could then twist them into a stem of wire to form a flower. Other activities included going out into the countryside along a canal towpath, me in the wheelchair, and playing games. I found the break refreshing and peaceful, and when I got back I felt much better, and for a while at least the depression passed.

Christmas drew near and with it the Junior Church carol service, which was an afternoon service the Sunday before Christmas. It was to be the debut service of the new-look Junior Church. We had been preparing well in advance. I had arranged Christmas songs on the keyboard and we had some dance and readings. Because my ME had been worse, we had taped the songs in case I couldn't make it. Throughout my ME, whenever I was doing anything, it was always touch and go whether I would make it or not. On that occasion I did, and I was glad because it went so well. It was different from any Christmas service we had done before. The young people taking part were enthusiastic and the people seemed to enjoy it even more than usual.

Playing in the service gave me a real lift mentally, and I was better that Christmas than I had been the previous year, although I always found Christmas with ME difficult because it reminded me that another year had gone by and I was still sick. Despite the fact that my ME had got worse through the winter, I hoped that 1992 would bring better things.

CHAPTER 8

Finding who my friends are

A long-term illness is something which affects not only the person suffering, but also the family: in my case my mum, dad and sister Alison. At first Dad found my illness and disability difficult to accept. It was as if he felt embarrassed about the way I walked and the fact that I was so ill. When we got the wheelchair he wasn't keen to take me out in it and that really used to annoy me because the only time I could get out of the area was when he was at home with the car. When he did get used to it, though, he was brilliant and gradually took me out more and more. We would go to country parks in the area, or to a craft shop for FIMO, or a Christian bookshop to buy a tape.

It was difficult, too, for Alison. At school she had to put up with people saying that her sister was a 'spastic'. Her friends didn't help by saying things like, 'ME? Don't you die of that?' She even thought we might be hiding the fact that I was going to die when, of course, we weren't, because I wasn't!

Sisters always argue. During my illness we still did, but in a slightly different form. Alison got jealous because I seemed to be getting more attention than she was, and I got angry with her because she could do all the things I couldn't — and still complained. Despite the arguments, though, we loved each other and didn't like to see the other hurting.

Then there was Mum, who really bore the brunt of my illness. Fortunately she didn't go out to work in the day, and so was at home to look after me. She was quite hard on me, and made me do as much as I could. That wasn't a bad thing, because I needed the motivation. If Mum hadn't been there I would have given up completely and stopped in bed all day. As it was, she encouraged me to do as much as possible, and helped me to plan events to look forward to, such as coffee mornings.

Through my illness I was dependent on Mum, as a small child would be. She walked miles, pushing me in the wheelchair; and when I did walk a short distance, I leaned on her. On bad days she would have to help me get dressed, have a bath, get around the house and even go to the toilet. Even on good days I could go nowhere without her or another adult I trusted and was close to, in case I was ill or my legs gave way. Of course we had our arguments and I sometimes used to feel stifled being with her so much. She probably felt the same about me, but without her I don't know how I would have coped.

When you are ill, particularly for a long time, you find out who your real friends are. There were two friends from school who particularly looked after me: Rebecca and Sally. At first I got visits from lots of friends. They usually came in a big group and invaded the living-room. As time went by, though, the number of visitors thinned out until as far as school was concerned, it was just Rebecca and Sally, though I did get other visitors from school occasionally. Despite studying for her GCSEs, Rebecca found time to visit me every week. I was very grateful for that because she was a contact with the goings-on at school. It can't have been easy for her. Some weeks I must have seemed very quiet and depressed, but she stuck by me.

The friendship with Sally was one which developed later in my illness. She always had, and still has, the ability to make me laugh. She is also a Christian and we could share things together to do with our faith. I thank God for providing me with such good and loyal friends.

I also made new friends with other young people who were sufferers too. It was surprising to find out how many of us there were in quite a small area. There was a parents' support group, too, which Mum and Dad joined, and they produced a register of young ME sufferers. I chose some names from the list of those who were my age or close to it, and wrote to them. In that way I made some pen-friends.

One of my best supporters was an 86-year-old lady. Her name was Beattie and she lived in our street and went to our church. I first became friendly with Beattie before my illness when I was working for a Girls' Brigade Community-Service Badge. Beattie was disabled as both her hips were artificial and she had to use two sticks to get around. She was a spinster so, having lived on her own for a long time, she was very independent and determined. For my badge I arranged to go to her house one afternoon each week after school to help with the housework. I was a bit nervous to start with, but she soon put me at ease. I enjoyed my time with her. We used to do various jobs together, cleaning out cupboards, polishing, dusting, and sometimes I would do some shopping for her, particularly if the weather was bad or she had been unable to go out for any other reason.

After we had worked for a while we would have a drink and sit and chat. She knew I liked a certain type of chocolate biscuit and made sure she always had some in the house. We discovered that despite the age gap we had a lot of interests in common. I can't remember my grandmas. They died when I was very young. My last grandparent, Poppa, had died the year before. Beattie began to fill a grandma's role for me. When my badge project was finished I continued to go to Beattie's regularly because I enjoyed my time with her so much. However, when I was ill I was unable to visit her very often, so she came to our house instead. Every Monday afternoon there was a Bible study at our house which she used to come to, and afterwards she would stop a while and talk to me. She would spoil me just as if I was her grandchild, saving sweets for me that she knew I liked, buying me a packet of my favourite biscuits, saving some of the best apples off her tree.

I am not the best person at saying how I feel, but one day I wrote Beattie a card and told her that I felt she was like my grandma. I wanted her to know how much I loved her. I'm glad I sent that card now. Beattie was such an example to me because she had so many difficulties with her hips and arthritis, yet she was always cheerful and always thought about other people and showed an interest in them. She was one of the people who helped to keep me going mentally with lots of encouragement.

Another person who was a major source of encouragement was my GP, Dr. Jill Stoner, who always had time for me, even though medically there was nothing she could do. When I was first ill, Dr. S. came to see me at home each week. That gradually spread out to once a fortnight, then once a month when I was well enough to get to the surgery. Dr. S. did everything she could to understand my illness. We took her magazines to read from the ME Association, and she would find out about any other thinking on the subject, and tell us about it. I found I could talk to her as a friend and not just as a doctor. When I was down she would talk things through with me. Having a sympathetic doctor made such a difference to me, and having her written backup when I needed it was vital for GCSE appeals and claiming benefits. She provided a much more positive image of doctors, and helped me not to have a completely negative view because of my previous experiences.

In the community there were so many good people who used to talk to me and obviously cared about me, that it would be impossible to mention them all. There was a local road sweeper who always used to have a word with us, and there were the elderly people in the day centre who used to wave as we went by, and many other people who would always stop and have a chat. When you are ill you discover how caring the majority of people are. I remember one example in particular. It was at a time when my walking had improved quite a lot and I could walk around a fairly big block. One day as we were about halfway round we passed a dustcart with dustmen all around tipping in the bins of rubbish. One of the dustmen suddenly said, 'Excuse me.' Both Mum and I wondered what he could possibly want. He continued: 'I want to congratulate you on your walking. I've often seen you as I've sat eating my dinner in the lorry at the end of the street, and I've noticed how much your walking has improved. It's really good. Well done!'

That one small incident really gave me a lift, and coming from a complete stranger the words had much more meaning than if they had come from somebody closer to me. That showed me just what a caring community I lived in, as did the way people supported my efforts to raise money for ME research.

Then there was my school. Apart from the way they helped me get my GCSEs, they also supported me in a caring way. Whenever I went, I was made to feel very welcome and various messages were sent home via Alison.

Last, but certainly not least, a major support from the community came from my church. The majority of my visitors were from church and whenever we were in need somebody would be there. I know that a lot of people were praying for our family throughout the time I was ill.

Our minister, Hazel, would help whenever she could. Although she was busy because of her job, she still found time to support us as a friend as well as a minister. She helped me forgive the people connected with my earlier, bad experiences with doctors. It was an important step. Before that I had felt a lot of bitterness. I still feel angry about what happened to me, but not bitter towards anyone in particular. When I was at Willersley, Hazel looked after me like a mother. She had a part in getting Sue and me together to pray, which I will deal with later on in this story.

I have already mentioned Sue in connection with the Junior Church, but she was also a very good friend and was there throughout my illness. I know she found many of the physical aspects of my illness difficult to cope with, but she never turned her back on me, as I felt some people did who couldn't cope. The friendship between Sue and me grew gradually throughout the time I was ill. She was also a very good friend to my mum. I didn't know about some of the things Sue did, nor how she was feeling about my illness until much later on. This is told in her own words in chapter sixteen.

I feel I could go on for ever talking about the people who were so good to me, but, of course, it is impossible to name them all. I am very grateful to everyone who helped me during my illness.

CHAPTER 9

Disturbing signs

One of the first things I did in 1992 was to get a Data disk to add to my keyboard. The problem was that whenever I produced something on the memory of the keyboard, I had to erase it to do the next song. As a result I could never keep any of my arrangements. By connecting the Data disk I could save whatever I wanted onto a computer disc. That meant I could store all the arrangements to form a library. The Data disk was easy to use and portable, so it was ideal. I could use the simple 8-track sequencer on the keyboard to its full potential.

Soon after I got the Data disk, I began to work on a Christmas musical which we were planning to use as part of a service for the following Christmas. I had agreed to arrange it on my keyboard, with Mum playing the piano as well. There was a lot of work involved in that, so I started a year in advance. By the end of February most of it was done. I was hoping that by Christmas I would be better and able to play. We had to plan ahead in the hope that I would be well, or at least much better by then, otherwise I wouldn't have done anything. I couldn't bear the thought of still being ill in a year's time.

The fourteenth of January was my seventeenth birthday and what a good day I had! I had a watch and CD from Mum and Dad, a tape and video from Alison, and lots of other good things. I had visitors all through the day and everybody did his or her best to make it special. I was fortunate in that I had a good day ME-wise, and despite my illness it was a birthday to remember, made so by many caring friends. That was to be my last high point for a while.

From then onwards it was downhill. The weather got

worse and so did my ME. I missed school a few times because of ice on the pavements, and when I did go it got more and more of a struggle. The last time I went for a lesson Mr. T. and another teacher nearly had to carry me to the taxi; and when I got home Mum had to do the same to get me into the house and onto my bed.

March the 1st is a date I shall always remember.

It was just an ordinary Sunday evening. One of Dad's friends was visiting us and we were watching a video. It was getting late so Mum and Alison went to bed. The video finished and I realized that I had become really tired while watching it. I knew that getting to bed was going to be a real effort, but I often felt like that. I sat, wishing I never had to move again. Then the exhaustion got worse. I felt as if I couldn't hold my head up, so I half lay down and put my head on the chair arm. The next moment I was spinning down a black hole and didn't have the energy to fight it. I could hear the TV droning on in the distance . . . Dad spoke: 'Come on, Kathryn; it's time for bed.' I managed to sit up and tried to say, 'I don't feel very well. I need some help,' but nothing came out. I couldn't speak at all. I couldn't get a single word out; it was as if my throat was paralysed.

Not being able to speak terrified me. A combination of the effort of sitting up and trying to speak made me gasp for breath. I had pins and needles down my right side and the sweat poured down my body. Gradually, the attack passed off, but I still couldn't speak and felt so ill. Obviously, Mum and Dad were alarmed as I hadn't had anything like that before, so they called the doctor. When he came I still couldn't speak and he didn't seem to have much idea why. For a while Mum stayed with me. I was frightened of being left on my own in case it happened again. When she did go, she left a tray by my bed and told me to bang it if I felt bad again. I slept all night.

The next morning I didn't feel quite as ill, but my voice

still wasn't there. That worried me in case it was permanent. Gradually, though, it came back, but it was very faint and sometimes I still had trouble getting words out. Speaking made me very breathless.

We saw Dr. S. and she sent me for a series of blood tests. Over the next two weeks I had attacks like the first one, but not quite as bad, every day. Each time I got the pins and needles, the breathlessness, the sweating and the shakes; and I lost my voice during the attack and for a short time afterwards. I got used to the warning signs and tried to make sure that I lay down as they came on. That seemed to help. I also managed to control the breathlessness a little, but still got all the other symptoms.

Another annoying thing which happened when I had an attack was that I always wanted the toilet desperately just afterwards. It was as if my bladder suddenly relaxed. We had to borrow a commode chair for after the attacks, and for the evening when I just couldn't get up the stairs. I hated having it in my bedroom and disguised it as much as possible. To my amusement, two of my friends on separate occasions said what a nice chair it was, and one even said she would have liked one in her bedroom! I had trouble keeping a straight face, but decided against enlightening her as its real use embarrassed me.

The blood tests showed that I had had mumps at some stage. That we already knew. I had had it when I was about 7. That was all. It is amazing how you can be so ill, yet nothing will show up. At the time I thought that my blood must be the most healthy part of me!

For the next month I was very ill and continued having the attacks most days. I spent a lot of time in bed, sometimes listening to books on tape, although a lot of the time I was too ill even for that. Mum didn't dare leave me on my own, so whenever she went out a friend would come and sit with me. Sue came and prayed with me as I lay in bed, but it didn't seem to have any effect. Even though a lot of people were praying for me, I felt as if God had abandoned me. It wasn't fair. I was having to start all over again from nothing. The only comfort to me was that I couldn't get any worse.

Again I was forced to let go of everything I had been working towards. It was impossible to consider doing GCSE exams. I felt so lonely. I had just started to mix with people a bit more by going in to school. I missed the outing and the regular morning a week with my tutor. I think that that was the absolute low of my illness. It was worse than the first time round because I knew how long improvement takes when you have ME. I couldn't imagine how I would ever get better. It felt as if the illness was going to go on for ever and that I would never be able to work, get married, or have a family as 'ordinary' people did.

Dr. S. could see how down I was, but even she seemed at a loss to know what to say. She was upset for us, having gone through it all with us for so long. There came a point when I just had to accept that I must start all over again. Dr. S. gave me some very gentle exercises, such as raising my legs off the bed and back down again. I gradually increased the number I could do. When I was well enough to get up, I would try to walk around the house or roll a ball under my feet. I had to aim for much smaller goals once more and be content with the slightest achievements. I was reassessed for my mobility allowance and could hardly walk at all. I knew I was worse than I had ever been, and the thought of how far I had to go filled me with despair. Sometimes I wished I could just go to sleep and never wake up.

I did improve, though. Through the spring my concentration made the biggest improvement. My legs were never as good again as they had been the previous summer. Music came to the rescue once more, and I wrote songs and pieces of music. I did more badge-making and jigsaws. Basically, I went back to the beginning, forgetting about school and just concentrating on making a slow improvement.

As soon as I felt well enough, I went back to Junior Church. I took a new song with me — 'Make Jesus number one'. It was a song I had written with the Junior Church in mind. They took to it and we decided to use it at the anniversary. Usually, practising for the Junior Church anniversary was a struggle. That year, though, we had a new image. We renamed the service 'Junior Church Celebration'. Instead of practising new songs, we decided to make use of the material we had introduced throughout the year. It would be different from any other year. There would be drama, singing with the keyboard, and refreshments afterwards with a display of artwork in the schoolroom.

Despite the fact that there was some improvement, the frustration I used to feel was often so intense that I wanted to throw things around. It sometimes used to seem as if everything I did was a complete waste of time. I never seemed to be able to complete anything or follow anything through. I would spend the day doing things which passed the time, but which, when analysed, were trivial and useless. When I did do something worthwhile, such as putting music onto my keyboard, I would feel frustrated because I wasn't well enough to use it anywhere. My illness restricted everything I did from the moment I woke up in the morning until the moment I fell asleep at night. The real me felt trapped and stifled by the symptoms. The constant, dull ache in my body wore me down. I often wished I could just get away from it.

Despite all of that, I did look forward to the anniversary. At least I would be able to use my music then. All I could do was pray that God would use what little I had for good. One way in which ME effectively changed my life was in giving me the incentive to do a lot more with my music than I probably would have done otherwise. Looking back I can see that during that time seeds were being sown for my playing in church. Gradually since then I have played in church more and more and my collection of songs on disk has grown. At the time, though, it was frustrating and I was very limited, but I just had to keep going.

CHAPTER 10

In the right direction

The Junior Church Celebration in May was my first major venture after my relapse. During the run-up to the anniversary, I borrowed the equipment and recorded the music for the songs on to tape. There would be two services, and I knew that at best I would cope only with one. At worst I might not be able to attend. Having a tape took the pressure off. The service could still go ahead. However, I really wanted to be a part of the services. Realistically, though, I knew that one service would be my limit. To do more would be to risk another relapse and there was no way I could face that.

At last it all came together. The morning service went well and I enjoyed playing in church. It was good to show the church what the Junior Church had been doing over the past year, and everyone seemed to enjoy it. At first I was going to walk into church and sit on a chair to play, but Mum persuaded me to be wheeled in and to stay in my wheelchair. That meant spending no more physical energy than necessary (the nerves and playing would take enough out of me), and at the end, when we knew I would be exhausted, I could be wheeled out of the side door quickly and taken home. That was what happened. I came home and went to bed; exhausted, but happy. I knew that it wasn't wise even to attempt the evening performance. I wouldn't have made it through, and to have to go out half way would have disrupted the proceedings and been worse than my not being there at all. I was learning not to push myself to the absolute limit. It only set me back. It wasn't worth it. This was a very hard lesson to learn; accepting that my illness was beating me went against the grain.

Another lesson I was learning was to accept small

achievements as victories. By the scale of my illness, getting to that one service and playing through the whole of it was a major achievement. On a day-to-day basis I had to set myself very small targets, and try not to look ahead too far. I found it extremely difficult. All my friends were thinking about university and careers.

People had come to accept me the way I was: ill and needing a wheelchair. It seemed as if the observation kept coming up: 'What about an electric wheelchair?' I can remember quite a number of people talking about electric wheelchairs. I was determined that there was no way I would have one. To me, that suggested permanence, and I couldn't cope with the thought. On the other hand, I often wondered. An electric wheelchair wouldn't have helped me much in that I couldn't have gone out on my own for fear of fainting, or not having the energy to get home, but I often felt guilty at Mum having to push me everywhere. I hated the thought of damaging her health too. I also hated being so dependent upon her. Yet I couldn't give in. An electric wheelchair was all right for other people, but not for me.

The fear of being stranded was always there. I became very dependent on my stick, psychologically as well as physically. I took it everywhere with me as I couldn't walk more than a few yards without it. At night I often dreamed of being without it and trying to get somewhere, usually in busy streets or trying to cross a road. Whereas near the beginning of my illness I had dreamt dreams where I could walk just like anybody else, it came to the place where I was even disabled in my dreams. I could hardly remember what it was like not to be so. The dreams were frightening and frustrating.

At home my illness had become the norm. I would fall over often and nobody would notice any more. I'm not complaining, but it was just a fact of life that I fell over a lot. To anybody outside it was a shock to see my legs fold under me, but to the family it was normal.

After the Junior Church Celebration, the next thing to look forward to was our holiday; but before then, something else began to happen. One day two friends came around, very excited about an idea they had had to start a youth group. While they had been at the Greenbelt Festival a few years previously, they had taken part in a special group which did different activities. The idea behind it was that the older teenagers organized the group for younger teenagers, and did all kinds of things such as drama, dance, music, singing and art, aiming to produce a concert. They had come up with the idea that we should run something similar ourselves. It sounded great.

At first we were so keen that we wanted to get going straight away, but as we calmed down we realized that a lot of work needed to be put in before we could do anything. We talked to other people about it, particularly those who might want to be leaders. We worked out what we would do, organized some music, wrote letters and asked for support. All through the summer we had regular meetings and made our plans. It was good for me to meet with my friends more often and I truly felt I was part of the group. I knew that if we did get things off the ground, my participation would be limited, but it would be good to mix with young people again, even if it wasn't every week.

At last the holiday came. Alison went away to Aunty Mary's on her own: she wanted a holiday away from us, away from me particularly, I think. Mum, Dad and I decided to go to another Aunty and Uncle's for our holiday. As always the first day was spent getting over the journey, but once that was accomplished, I had a brilliant time. We managed to get out a little. I did some shopping for clothes and we went to the coast. The weather was fairly good. I felt happy and very peaceful, and wished that the holiday would never end. It had to, of course, and things had to get back to normal. At that time I began to feel I had really come to terms with my illness. I could cope with the bad days as long as I made the most of the good ones. I felt very happy going on small outings. They wouldn't have satisfied an ordinary, healthy 17-year-old, but to me they were a bonus each time. Maybe some of the fight had gone out of me. I accepted that I was as I was, and tended not to think of the future much at all. It only depressed me if I did. I stopped pushing myself as hard, because the relapse had frightened me. I no longer walked every day or tried to get a bit further each time. I just walked on good days whatever distance I could manage. Having said that, I do not mean that I had given up. I still tried to do things, to aim for events and to make something useful.

The next fund-raising project was decided. As mentioned before, every year at school there is a craft fair held during October. That year I planned to have a stall and put all my badges, key-rings, ear-rings, etc., on display. The idea was to raise money from a different group of people from the ones who supported the coffee mornings — mainly church people and those from the local community. People came from other places to the school craft fair. I was getting adept at making the badges, often baking a trayful in a day.

Through the summer my physical improvement was very slow, and my walking barely improved. I was finding, though, that my concentration was a lot better and I felt ready to have another go at studying. I didn't kid myself into believing that I could cope with an exam, however, because I wasn't expecting to make that much of an improvement. By then I knew that winter was a bad time for ME patients, so my aim for the winter was simply to be careful not to push myself. The least I could do was keep from getting worse. Of course, I couldn't really control my condition, but I was getting better at observing my body's warnings and giving up before I reached the point of complete collapse. I decided to complete my GCSE History course at home. When I found I could cope with this, I began to consider doing a correspondence course.

I wrote away for some leaflets and looked at the list of subjects. There was no point in taking any more GCSEs as I had the five I needed. It made sense to go on to do an A-level. At first I thought about English Literature, but when I saw how many books were on the reading list, I realized it wouldn't be a good idea because of my eye problems. In the end I settled for Sociology. A friend had just taken it and she had enjoyed the course. Within a few weeks a big parcel was delivered to the front door. The course consisted of two large A4 folders of work. In some ways seeing all that work in front of me was a bit daunting. Mainly it was exciting and challenging to be starting a new course. I could take up to three years to complete it. I didn't know if I would be able to take the exam at the end, but three years' time was a long way ahead and I couldn't see that far. The main thing was to be doing something right then.

When I started the course, I realized that the standard was higher than GCSE and it took a while to adjust to the more advanced language and concepts. Although it was hard work, I enjoyed studying again and found that my concentration had definitely improved. On a good day I could manage an hour's work. Doing some studying in the morning gave a point to the day, and I felt a sense of achievement in learning new things. Also, I was no longer just marking time as far as my education was concerned. I may have been left behind by my friends, but at least I was moving in the right direction.

CHAPTER 11

SHOUT! – and a healing service

The summer was ending. It hadn't been a particularly good one weather-wise, and ME-wise I hadn't made as much improvement as the previous year. The winter lay ahead, and it felt as if I was about to enter a long, dark tunnel. I knew from previous experience that I could expect no improvement until the spring. My course helped. At least it would be something to do through the winter. Also my crafts continued in preparation for the craft fair at school. Practices started for the Christmas musical. I didn't go to the first few because the choir needed to learn the songs with just the piano accompaniment.

During September I really got stuck into my course and seemed to be doing quite well. Then on 24 September Beattie died. Even though she was elderly it came as a shock because it happened so suddenly. She hadn't been as well as usual for a while, but one morning she was found collapsed in her house. She was taken into hospital and died the next day. The week before, Mum and I had called in to see her and she had been her old self. I suppose I knew in my heart that she wouldn't always be there, but you like to imagine people can go on for ever. I couldn't go to the funeral because of my ME.

At about the same time as Beattie died, Dr. S. announced that she was leaving. Dr. S. and Beattie were the two people who had encouraged me all the way through my illness. Suddenly I had lost both in a very short time. I wondered how I could possibly cope without them, and suddenly felt very lonely and depressed. As far as I was concerned, I had lost a grandparent and a very good friend. Whenever I had been down, usually Beattie or Dr. S. had helped raise my spirits. Having neither to lean on, I felt as though I could never be happy again. I was sick of being ill and tired of being cut off from the world.

During October Mum was due to go into hospital for an operation. I knew that afterwards she wouldn't be able to push me in the wheelchair for at least a couple of months. That didn't help my general depression. I would be stuck in the house even more. I knew it was selfish of me to think like that and, of course, I cared about Mum, but it made the coming winter seem even darker. To try to counteract the gloom, we planned that soon after Mum came out of hospital I would go to my Aunty Florence and Uncle Eric's for a week. That would serve three purposes. It would give me something to look forward to. It would give me a break from the same four walls. It would mean that Mum could relax without having to worry about me. In fact, it would be a break for both of us. Despite having this to look forward to, I still felt miserably low.

A couple of weeks before I was due to go away, there was a healing service at church and I decided to go. To be honest, I went more because of my depression than expecting to be healed physically. During the service I went forward. After communion I stayed at the rail with other people and the team of leaders laid hands on us and prayed. It was a very emotional experience, after which I felt the depression lifting. I started to feel better inside and began to look forward again to the break away from home.

Mum had to be in hospital only overnight for her operation, and although she was obviously ill and had to be in bed for a while, everything seemed to have gone smoothly.

The journey to Aunty Florence and Uncle Eric's is just under two hours by car. Dad drove me half-way and Uncle Eric met us and took me the other half.

I had some of my A-level work and crafts with me to do during the mornings when Aunty Florence would be at work. My cousin Adrian had booked a couple of days off work so he would be home those days. I took it quite easy and rested because I didn't want the journey to affect me. Despite that, on the third evening I took a sudden turn for the worse. Feeling tired in the evening, I went up to my room and lay on the bed for a while. The time passed and I decided to get ready for bed. I walked with a lot of difficulty to the wash basin and cleaned my teeth. Putting away my toothbrush, I felt one of my fainting attacks coming on and fell to the floor. Since the end of March these attacks had become less frequent and this was the first one I'd had for a couple of months. All the familiar symptoms came over me. I had to bang on the floor because I couldn't speak or shout. Adrian rushed upstairs to see what the banging was, and when he saw me in a heap on the floor he fetched Aunty Florence. I couldn't talk to explain what was happening, but she knew about the fainting attacks. She helped me into bed, stayed for a while, and then made sure I was all right by looking in on me later. She was very kind, but I didn't like having to be undressed and taken to the toilet by someone other than Mum. The only person who ever did those things for me had been Mum, and up to that time no one outside the immediate family had seen me in such a state.

The next morning I stayed in bed. Aunty and Uncle were really good to me and tried to help as best they could. Uncle Eric fixed up my portable television so that I could watch it from bed. I had some breakfast, then Aunty Florence had to go to work. It was one of Adrian's days off. This made it particularly disappointing because I would rather have spent the day with him than lie in bed feeling terrible.

I cried because I wanted Mum. It wasn't anything that my relatives had done or not done, but on a bad day I just wanted her. I would have given anything to have been in my own bed. I thought about ringing her up, but knew that if I did I would break down and then she would worry about me, and she wasn't well either. I worried that I had suffered a relapse like the one in the previous March, and the thought of experiencing more fainting attacks and having to start from scratch again frightened me.

By midday I felt well enough to go downstairs and Adrian looked after me, getting me some dinner. I spent the rest of the day on the settee.

Fortunately, my fears of a relapse did not materialize and I improved through the rest of the week. We managed to go out a little and I enjoyed myself. It was good to be in different company and in a different house. Aunty Florence is an artist and she let me use some of her paints. It was good to try out something new. I phoned home when I was feeling much better and found that Mum had been ill, too; she had an infection. I was glad then that I hadn't phoned when I was at my lowest; at least I was in a position to tell her not to worry as I was all right. The holiday came to an end, as holidays will, and apart from that one bad day it had been a success. I was glad that I had been away, but now it was time to get back to everyday life at home.

It was only a few days before another big event: the first night of our youth group. Since the initial idea in the summer our plans had progressed. We had regular meetings and had built up a group of about eight leaders. After meeting with our minister, Hazel, she presented our ideas to the church council meeting. It was passed. We were allowed to start the group. Next we had to put up posters to advertise our starting date and plan the fine details. We also decided on a name for our group; SHOUT. When the words of our logo, 'Jesus Hears Our Young Teens', are placed under one another as an acrostic, the name SHOUT is highlighted:

JE**S**U**S**

HEARS

OUR

YO**U**NG

TEENS

We would meet every Friday night from seven to nine for games, dance, drama, music, crafts, etc., and also have outings. The creative work would go towards concerts and participation in church services. Each Friday night we would have a time of devotions when a member of our church would come in and lead a short time of Bible reading and prayer.

The first night came and we were excited and nervous. It all went quite well. Another church's youth group joined us for that evening to see what it was all about, and we had some other young people, but they were all folk who already came to church. We had been hoping to attract some youth who didn't normally come, so we were a bit disappointed. That evening we had about twelve altogether.

Gradually the group grew and we were pleased with the way it was going. Unfortunately, because of my ME, I wasn't always able to attend, and when I was there I could cope only with an hour or so. The others were good, though, and made me feel part of it all.

At the same time as the club was getting off the ground, I was attending rehearsals for the Christmas musical. I found it hard work. It was taxing both physically and mentally, but I enjoyed playing the keyboard. It had gone this far and I needed to see it through.

In October I had a stall at my school's craft fair as planned, and raised more money for ME research. It was something I had wanted to do for a long time, and it was different. We took photographs of the stall and I felt a great sense of achievement.

Things were getting better again. The depression abated for a month or two as plans were seen through. There were other things to look forward to as well. The church weekend at Willersley was coming round again in January, as was my eighteenth birthday. I had decided to have an open house on my birthday, for people to call in. Then there would be a family day on the Saturday of the same week when all the relatives could come.

I had my mind set on acquiring some recording equipment so that whenever I produced anything I could back it up by recording it in case I was too ill to be at the function. I was also very interested in multi-track recording and wanted to put my songs and compositions on tape.

I started looking at other keyboards. I decided it might be best to sell my two small ones and the disk player, and buy one really good keyboard with an in-built disk drive. I saw one which I really liked the look of and fell in love with it. I had to get it. We planned to get both the keyboard and recording equipment just after Christmas, but the recording equipment would be put aside until my birthday. Something to look forward to.

A strange thing happened in the November which I can now only look back on with amazement. Mum wrote down the date because she felt it was significant. That day, 19 November, was completely ordinary, just like any other, except for one statement that my dad made. He, Alison and I were sitting in the living-room, and Mum was teaching the piano in the other room. I can't remember what we were doing, or what we were talking about, but Dad suddenly said: 'You're going to get better.'

I don't know what it was about the way he said it; maybe it was the conviction in his voice; but my heart jumped.

'What do you mean?' I asked.

'You're going to get better. I know you are,' he answered.

'How do you know?'

'I know.'

He was obviously a bit embarrassed and wouldn't reveal how he 'knew', except that he had had some kind of experience.

All the time I was ill, people had said things to me about getting better, such as 'You will get better, won't you, . . . eventually?' and, 'Oh, we'll have you running round the block one day' or, 'You'll probably wake up one morning and find that it's gone as quickly as it came.'

It had not come on particularly quickly, but that had not affected the popularity of the theory. I had never taken such statements seriously. They were usually made by people who didn't know anything about ME anyway, and didn't know what else to say. I always tended to avoid the subject of getting better. It was something I vaguely thought would happen one day, but not just then.

My future was always very hazy in my mind. It was as if I didn't dare think about getting better. It was too much like a dream; and I felt I had to prepare myself for the possibility of not getting better to avoid disappointment. Not that that worked! Somehow, though, I believed Dad. He was never the sort to make shallow statements without proof, but that wasn't all. It was as if he spoke with some kind of authority; and, from that moment on, something changed inside me. It was as if a switch had been thrown in my brain, and I began to think about the future.

Over the next few days I questioned Dad: 'How? When? . . . .' He said he thought it would be soon, but not straight away. 'Do you think it might be after Christmas?' I persisted. 'Some time around my birthday?'

'Yes,' he said, 'it should be about that time.'

I spoke to Mum and to my surprise found that Dad hadn't said anything to her about it. I think maybe he found it easier in some ways to talk to me because I was younger and a less experienced Christian. Before that, Dad hadn't really been into 'church'. He believed in God, but religion wasn't for him, except on special occasions. He found it embarrassing to talk about his experience. *He said he would tell us about it when I got better.*

From that time on I began to plan. I said: 'When I get better I'm going to have a party. When I get better I'm going to walk and walk. When I get better we shall have a thanksgiving service. When I get better I will be able to do anything. When I get better . . . .' I felt so happy, even though my ME wasn't improving. Mum encouraged me. She could see it was making me happy and keeping me going.

Only a few weeks ahead, though, was another low.

CHAPTER 12

Only a dream

It was the beginning of Advent, and the time for the musical drew near. We were to perform it at our church in an evening service, but a week beforehand we presented it at another church. I knew it was going to take a lot out of me, and was very careful for several weeks not to overdo my activities and risk a relapse. We had borrowed equipment to record the songs I was going to play by myself, so that if I couldn't cope, at least some of the keyboard items would be recorded and my work not completely wasted.

The first evening came and I felt well enough to go for it. Before the service I sat in the vestry suffering from nerves. My hands always go cold when I am nervous, which isn't very helpful when you are a piano or keyboard player. That evening was no exception and Mum kept rubbing them to try to warm them. Once we got in, though, time went very quickly and I didn't notice how I felt because I was concentrating so hard on the music. At the end Mum wheeled me straight out to avoid the noise and people, and Dad loaded the equipment into the car. At home I lay on the bed as Mum undressed me, helped me under the quilt, and brought me a drink. I felt as though I had given everything that evening. I was completely exhausted and mentally drained.

During the week that followed, I was very ill and spent a lot of time in bed. But each day I improved a little and kept up my hopes of playing again the next Sunday at our own church. After all the work I had put in, I couldn't stand the thought of not taking part.

Sunday came and I decided I could go ahead. The musical itself went very well. I felt that I played slightly better than the week before. I was more relaxed, probably because it was in our own church. I got to the end of the last song and it was only then, when the musical was over, that it really hit me. I felt so sick and exhausted, as though I hardly had the strength to sit up in my wheelchair. Mum wheeled me out of the side door as planned and somehow I struggled into the front seat of the car. I literally had to crawl from our front door to my bedroom.

That night was one of the lowest points of my illness. I ached, felt sick and was so exhausted I could hardly move. Mentally I was at my lowest. I cried because I felt frustrated and angry — and so ill. Once more I wished I could go to sleep and never wake up again.

During the weeks before Christmas I couldn't do anything. I missed the Junior Church carol service, and didn't go to the Shout group. I was very down. Mum tried to help me get over it by talking about my eighteenth birthday and making it something to look forward to. Gradually my health improved and I became less depressed. Then I began to be excited at the thought of the new keyboard and recording equipment. At the back of my mind, though, was the niggling thought that another year had passed and I was no better. Once my birthday was over I wondered how I could cope, looking ahead to another empty year of illness.

The main thing I remember about Christmas 1992 was buying the new equipment. First of all we went to the shop and had a demonstration on the keyboard in which I was interested. We were also shown the multi-track recording equipment and were able to price it. The next time we went, we bought it all. I was allowed to have the keyboard straight away, but the 4-track recorder was put away until my birthday. I had traded in my old equipment, but the new keyboard was bigger and better than any I had played before. I had to be careful not to overdo it, but played as often as I could. There was so much to explore and learn about my new instrument. I found I could do a lot more with it and produce better sounds and arrangements. Whenever I played, the time would fly.

While that was happening, I was having to make unpleasant decisions. I had to decide finally to let go of my History GCSE. I had been working on it through the autumn, but yet again I had little hope of being well enough to take the exam. I decided it would be much better to concentrate on the Sociology A-level which would take me at least another year.

The next event was the Willersley weekend. The previous year I had gone on my own when a place had been cancelled at the last minute. The visit had helped me a lot. A year later we were going as a family, and I was looking forward to it.

As before, the weekend was booked for the same church group. When we got there I walked to the room I would be sharing with Alison and a friend, and then, after unpacking, we went down to the lounge where people were mingling as they arrived. There was dinner and then a fun social with various couples taking part in a quiz game. It was very noisy! I had to leave early because as usual it got too much. My legs had given way so Mum had to take me up to the room in my wheelchair.

The next morning my legs were really bad. They shook and wobbled so that I couldn't keep my balance or even support myself. As usual, it took me a while to come round, so I couldn't manage any breakfast. Later, though, I felt quite good in myself, despite the fact that my legs were useless. At one point I actually fell over when trying to move from a seat to my wheelchair and felt very stupid.

I had to prove that I could do something so I had a game of table tennis with Dad. It was surprising that I could play quite well sitting down. It gave me a sense of achievement to be doing something normal, so I had another game with somebody else, then another. Needless to say, I suffered for it next day with painful arms and shoulders, but I didn't mind. At least I'd done something.

Later, Mum took me out in the wheelchair to a few shops, and then I had a rest in bed. Although I missed out on the Saturday night social, afterwards we played a game until midnight and, apart from my legs, I wasn't too bad at all. Looking back, I believe it was almost as if people had to see how bad my legs were. Normally, if my legs were that bad I would have been ill in myself as well, and would have stopped in bed where nobody would have seen me. I think that maybe a few people were made more aware of my condition over that weekend.

On the Sunday my legs remained bad and I was still also suffering from my table-tennis exploits. I ate hardly any breakfast and found it difficult to eat lunch. I had a sleep while everyone else was in the afternoon service. Then we came home.

Despite the problems, I enjoyed Willersley a lot. It was good to spend some time away from home in the fellowship of our friends.

After Willersley it was only a few days until my birthday on 14 January. We had an open house as planned, and I had visitors from ten o'clock in the morning until ten o'clock at night! They were mainly friends from church and school, and they all helped to make it a very special day. I had two birthday cakes specially made, one fruit and one sponge (I only like sponge!). I cut the fruit cake on my birthday and saved the sponge until the weekend when we were planning to have the family party. I ended the day tired but very happy. The next day I rested and tried to store up my energy for Saturday.

It was fortunate that Saturday was another good day ME-wise. Gradually, all the family arrived and soon we had a houseful of people. I received even more presents and cards, showed off what I already had, and demonstrated my keyboard to those who were interested. Again it was a really good, if tiring day. Despite my ME I managed to celebrate my eighteenth birthday, and shall always remember it as a happy time.

With my birthday celebrations over, I wondered what my nineteenth year held in store for me. I wondered how the year 1993 would turn out. To be honest, my expectations weren't very high. I hoped I would improve through the year, but didn't expect anything too dramatic. Of course, I always dreamt of waking up one morning fit and well, but that was all it was — a dream that was very unlikely to happen. If I was going to get better it would be a slow, uphill struggle with highs and lows, good weeks and bad. That was what I expected.

CHAPTER 13

A healer, but not a Christian

A couple of days after the family party, Mum spoke to me about something that my Aunty Florence had said to her on the Saturday. Apparently, Aunty had heard about a healer in her area who had healed a man of ME. She had asked Mum to discuss it with me, and to contact her if I wanted to find out more. We talked about it and I decided I did want to find out more. There was nothing to lose. Aunty Florence investigated further and found that the man didn't charge for what he did. He had discovered that he had a gift and wanted to use it to help people. When he took somebody on to be healed, he or she had to go to him every day for about five weeks. He had no religious beliefs.

I had been praying that the man would be a Christian healer because I believed that those kinds of healing powers came from God and should be acknowledge for what they were. When I found out he wasn't a Christian it troubled me straight away.

The decision was up to me. The next stage, if I wanted it, was to contact the man and see if he would take me on but, before that, I had to decide if it was what I wanted. I talked to Mum and Dad about it, but they wouldn't advise me because they both said it was my decision and they couldn't make it for me.

Practically, it was quite feasible. I could go and stay at Aunty Florence and Uncle Eric's for five weeks and visit the man each day. I said that if I went I would want Mum to come with me. Mum and Dad said that could all be worked out if I wanted it.

The main problem was that the man wasn't a Christian. It wasn't that I held it personally against him, or that what he was doing was wrong. I didn't know what to think really; for me it was a problem. I felt it would be very difficult to put any faith in a person rather than in God.

For the next week the two halves of my mind fought with each other. My ME got worse and I felt very depressed. One half of my mind said: 'Why should the fact that he isn't a Christian be so important? If a doctor had come up with a new drug that would cure ME I would take it whether he was a Christian or not. What's the difference? Anyway, surely it doesn't matter; getting well is what matters. Imagine being well after five weeks!'

The other half of my mind would then argue back: 'It does matter that he isn't a Christian because I believe that God gives those kinds of gifts and that it is God, not the person, who heals. This is different from medical science. . . . Doing what God wants is more important than being well. Anyway, there is no guarantee this man would heal me.'

On top of that ongoing argument was the overwhelming desire to get well. It was the thing I wanted most in the world. Of course I wanted to be well and to lead a normal life again. I got very confused. If I went to the man and was healed, would it be against God's will? Didn't God want me to be healed?

I tried to convince myself that it could be God's will for me to go to this man and be healed. I remembered what Dad had said about my getting better and thought that here was the opportunity. It could be God's plan. Yet in the back of my mind was a little voice, saying, 'No. It's wrong!' and I couldn't make it go away. I even got angry with God because of what Dad had been saying. Right then he was getting closer to becoming a Christian, but I felt that if I didn't become well, it would put him off forever. Because of that I felt under pressure and couldn't understand what God was doing. I argued with myself and prayed until I was completely confused, yet I knew that I had somehow to come to a decision.

It was so difficult. It was as though the thing I longed for most was being dangled in front of me, yet I was unable to take it. I wanted to take it so much that it hurt.

In the end I made my decision. I wouldn't go unless I somehow received a sign that I was meant to go. If it was God's will, then I prayed He would make it clear. I don't know exactly what kind of sign I expected or hoped for, but it never came.

As soon as I had made a decision it was as if an enormous weight was lifted from my heart. The depression passed and my ME returned to normal. My mind felt clearer and I was sure I had done the right thing. I remembered how happy I had felt when Dad had said I was going to get better, yet the business of the healer had only made me feel miserable and confused. Why? Because in my heart I knew that it wasn't right.

So I came to the conclusion that if it was God's will that I should be healed by that man, He would make it clear, or He would heal me by using a Christian.

It seemed as if my chance for a miracle had gone. I believed God could heal me, but didn't really think that He would. That was something which only happened to other people: a friend of a friend or somebody in a book or on television. It was very unlikely anything like that would ever happen to me. I resigned myself to facing my illness on a continual day-to-day basis.

During the time I was going through the decision-making process, Mum went to see Hazel, our minister. Something Hazel said made Mum think. She said it would be good to ask Sue to come and pray with me on a regular basis. Mum suggested it to me and I agreed. I think Mum thought that praying with Sue would be a good support for me mentally after the trauma of the decision-making I had just gone through. The prayer should strengthen me to face the facts. Maybe I felt like that too, but the need for Sue to come suddenly seemed urgent and I couldn't concentrate on anything else.

The following Saturday there was a worship workshop and meal at church, and I decided to go to part of it. During the meal I was sitting next to Sue and was dying to say something to her, but Mum had said she would speak to her after the Sunday evening service.

I asked Sue, 'Will you be coming around sometime?'

She said 'Yes' in a vague sort of way. She probably wondered what I was going on about. As always I had to leave early because of tiredness. I pestered Mum over and over to make sure she asked Sue. At last Sunday evening came.

Mum arrived home a long time after the service had finished so I guessed that she had been talking to Sue. She said that Sue had agreed to come on a weekly basis to pray with me. She went on to say that Sue had been amazed because she had actually been praying about what she should do. Sue had been feeling for a long time that she ought to pray with me; but more recently she felt she had a gift and had been praying for God to use her. What Mum had said to her seemed like an answer to prayer.

I was relieved that Sue had agreed, and very happy that she was coming. Looking back, I'm not sure why I was so keen, as I had no idea what was going to happen next. I wasn't expecting anything special at all. Maybe the feeling came because it was more like following God's will and seemed right.

We asked Sue to come the next Thursday and then, hopefully, every week afterwards when possible.

The days seemed to pass slowly until Thursday came.

CHAPTER 14

Sue's prayer
and miraculous happenings

Thursday 28 January 1993.

I had breakfast, got up and dressed. Then I decided to do some of my A-level work. I carried it in, opened the books at the relevant pages, but just couldn't do it. I felt the usual exhaustion and poor concentration of a bad day and resignedly shut the books, took them into my room, and got back into bed. After an hour or so in bed and a sleep, I realized that the day was a no-go day and put my pyjamas on. I slept and rested all day, apart from about an hour at lunch time. I woke for a while in the evening and was sitting in the chair in my room, still in my pyjamas, when Sue came. We talked for a while about the various events leading to our meeting, and she shared some of what she had read in a book that day which seemed particularly relevant to her and to our situation.

We both felt it was right to be praying that evening, but I don't think either of us expected the miracle that was going to happen in the next few days. We read a passage from the *Good News Bible*, Ephesians 6, the whole armour of God, verses 14-18:

'So stand ready, with truth as a belt tight around your waist, with righteousness as your breastplate, and as your shoes the readiness to announce the Good News of peace. At all times carry faith as a shield; for with it you will be able to put out all the burning arrows shot by the Evil One. And accept salvation as a helmet, and the word of God as the sword which the Spirit gives you. Do all this in prayer, asking for God's help. Pray on every occasion, as the Spirit leads. For this reason keep alert and never give up; pray always for all God's people.'

Sue held my hand as she prayed with me and I had a strange but pleasant sensation going up my arm and into my body. I felt so peaceful that I wished it could go on and on. I felt my head rising up from the crouching forward position I was in, to lying backwards in my chair. I also had a strange sensation in my chest and immediately afterwards was aware that my heart, which had been beating furiously, had quietened and slowed down. At the time, although I felt uplifted spiritually, I didn't think anything had happened physically.

After Sue left I lay in bed and prayed for a long time before I went to sleep. I felt as if there were some things I had to say to God. I didn't think I had been healed, but it wasn't too much of a disappointment because my expectations hadn't been very high. I had never expected to be suddenly healed. I had the idea that if I was healed it would be a gradual process, lasting about a year. To me, the thought of being well in a year was good.

Basically, in my prayer I said to God: 'My life is Yours whatever happens. If I am healed I will do my best for You. If not, I will still do my best for You.'

I drifted to sleep peacefully and Thursday ended. I had absolutely no idea what was ahead, or that I had just had my last day with ME.

Friday 29 January.

When I got up on Friday morning I was aware of an inner energy that I found hard to understand because I couldn't remember having it before. I was very restless all day and couldn't seem to relax. In the afternoon Mum took me out in the wheelchair to the library to get some books for Alison who was off school ill. On the way back I was so restless I said to Mum, 'I want to throw away my wheelchair!'

She answered, 'Perhaps one day you will.'

When we got to the top of the street I decided that I

wanted to get out of the chair and walk. I had my stick, but I didn't seem to need it much as I walked with ease down the length of the street. At the end I wasn't even tired, but I didn't dare do any more for fear of exhausting myself because I wanted to attend Shout Group that night. Mum suggested that I had a rest in bed before tea so as to be all right for Shout. I agreed and went to bed, but ten minutes later I was up again. I didn't feel as if I needed a rest because I was full of energy. I can remember thinking: 'Maybe this is the start of a recovery. Maybe Sue's prayers marked the turning point?' My brain, though, was thinking in the time scale of, 'This time next year I might be better.'

The visit to the library inspired me to start reading a book. To read was as much a test of my ME as the walking had been.

I now think that if I had tried to do more, tried to walk further, I would have found out more quickly that I was healed. As it was, my brain was continuing as normal and couldn't grasp what an amazing thing was happening to me.

In the evening I went to Shout and left early as usual. Normally after an hour-and-a-half I would have been exhausted, but I felt fine. I went to bed, taking my tablets as usual, still not realizing what was happening.

Saturday 30 January.
The next morning I still felt full of energy. In the afternoon, Friday's success made me decide to walk up the street and back. Mum came with me as usual and Alison came too. After a week off school she wanted a breath of fresh air. We started out and I went so fast that I left Mum and Alison behind! Instead of just walking the street, I walked the whole block! I had no ill effects and finished the day feeling good.

Sunday 31 January.

I would say that Sunday was in a way a turning point, for it was Sunday when I actually began to realize what was happening to me. In the morning I wanted to walk across to church with my stick, but mum discouraged me because I was playing my keyboard in the service, and was hoping to stay for the whole time, which would be an achievement in itself. I agreed and decided not to walk. I played my keyboard and then sat through the whole service; my legs were fine. In fact, I felt fine altogether.

After lunch I decided to tackle the block again. I got halfway around as easily as I had the day before. Finally I realized I just didn't need the stick! I handed it to my surprised Mum, saying, 'I don't need this. Please carry it.'

I walked the rest of the way with ease and felt as if I could have walked much further. I didn't dare go out again, though, for fear of overdoing it and making myself ill again. Yet in my mind I began to believe that it was just possible I had been healed. I decided to test it out. Reasoning that if the ME had really gone I would be able to sleep without my night tablet, I wouldn't take it, but if I wasn't asleep by midnight I would get up and take one. I didn't tell Mum my plan because I thought she would lie awake worrying. I even went into the kitchen and took a drink of water to complete the pretence.

Lying in bed, wondering if I would sleep, I made it very difficult for myself because I was so excited. Every time I started to drop off I woke myself up, thinking, 'Yes, I'm doing it! I'm going to sleep!' I was just beginning to think I would never get off, when I fell asleep at last. It must have been about 11.30pm.

Monday 1 February.

I finally woke at 5.40am. I had slept fairly lightly and was aware of having woken briefly several times during the night, but the euphoria that swept over me was amazing.

The sleeping test just made me sure my ME was on the way out. It could even have gone altogether! I felt as if I had tons of energy and the joy was bubbling inside me. I went and listened outside Mum and Dad's door. Hearing Mum stir, I went in. I was too excited to keep to myself the news that I had slept without a tablet.

I decided to keep a diary. It was quite brief, but the following days' comments are extracts from the book, which gives an idea of my progress from then on.

Monday 1 February.

Slept through the night without tablet. Walked around the whole of Butt Street block (further than yesterday) without even taking stick, at normal walking speed with no difficulty. I've done quite a lot of reading.

Tuesday 2 February.

Slept through the night without tablet again, a really good, deep sleep, better than last night's. Walked to the library and back, leaving stick at home. In the afternoon walked right around Woodside Estate (a much further and very hilly walk) on my own and was amazed how easy it felt. Sally came in the afternoon after school — what a surprise for her to find out what had happened. Rang around the relatives and close friends in the evening.

As you can probably tell, Tuesday was the day I finally accepted my complete healing. The excitement and joy is hard to describe. It was like living in some wonderful dream. I felt like a person out of a book. I could hardly believe that a miracle so wonderful could have happened to me!

Wednesday 3 February.

Walked up to school in the morning (about a mile uphill!) to surprise all the staff. Mr. T's reaction was brilliant — I wish I'd had a video camera! On the way home from school I called at a friend's house.

In the afternoon I was a bit quieter, but felt so restless and found it hard to sit down quietly for more than ten minutes! I watched the football until midnight. I was tired, of course, after a busy day, but only tired — there were none of the awful ME symptoms and, of course, I slept without tablets. I can hardly believe it: tablets, sticks and wheelchairs are actually becoming things of the past. A new life is ahead of me. I feel so joyful and can't stop praising God for what He has done for me. I will never doubt miracles again.

The joy I felt was incredible. I felt as though I could fly! I jumped around the house and tired my family out. The happiness just bubbled out of me and I couldn't help telling everybody what had happened. I met people in the community and they couldn't believe their eyes. I was walking and talking like a new person. My face suddenly had colour. I look at photographs now of 'before' and 'after', and can see the difference.

Thursday 4 February.

It has been a week since Sue was here and she came again today. I hadn't seen her since Sunday but had rung her on Monday to tell her what was happening. I shared it all again with her, then we went out for a walk. I wanted to demonstrate what I could do.

Friday 5 February.

Went to Shout as usual, but without my wheelchair. One of my friends didn't know anything about what had been happening and she could hardly believe it. After Shout I went out with the group for the first time. It was so good to go out with people of my own age.

Over the next few weeks I wrote to my old school friends with whom I was still in touch, and began to plan. I decided I wanted to have a Thanksgiving Service, followed by a party at church. I chose the hymns and songs, and arranged them on my keyboard. I met with Hazel and discussed what I wanted her to say. I chose readings and also a song which I wanted to be played in the service. It was the one based on the words of Isaiah which I had clung to for so long:

'He strengthens those who are weak and tired. Even those who are young grow weak; young men can fall exhausted. But those who trust in the Lord for help will find their strength renewed. They will rise on wings like eagles; they will run and not get weary; they will walk and not grow weak.'

We had the Thanksgiving Service in March, on a Saturday afternoon. In the morning we set it all up. We put a cassette player in the church and in the hall hung balloons and set out tables and chairs ready for the party.

The Thanksgiving Service went well and I enjoyed it. All went according to plan. The most important thing was that we acknowledged what God had done for me and praised Him for it.

After the service the party began. We had a buffet tea followed by games. It was a really good party with the church family. So ended a memorable day.

The next day the celebration continued when Dad walked in with a beautifully-decorated cake he had secretly had made especially for me. It had my name on and a picture of a piano iced on the top.

After the many lows of my illness, all the happiness of being well again was the highest feeling I have ever experienced, and I doubt I will ever have a feeling quite like it again.

Suddenly, life in its fullness opened up before me.

CHAPTER 15

Restored

Being healed is the best thing that has ever happened to me. It was the thing I dreamt of, yet never thought would happen. I can't imagine a better feeling than when I walked on my own for the first time in two-and-a-half years.

Being healed, though, brought about enormous changes both physically and psychologically, and in many ways was as difficult to adjust to as when I first became ill. Although being well is a much more pleasant state to adjust to, it still has its problems, which I would never have thought of unless I had experienced such a dramatic change. In the Bible stories of Jesus' miracles of healing, you never hear about what happened to the people afterwards, and how they adapted to the amazing changes in their life. I found that once the miracle had happened I had to go on from there and start to live again.

The first two weeks after being healed were the best of my life. I was constantly on a high and buzzed with energy and happiness. During the third week I suddenly began to think about what I was doing, and my confidence wobbled a bit. When I went out on my own I felt insecure, and worried about simple things like crossing the road. For more than two years I hadn't been out on my own. Now it felt strange to be independent and making my own decisions. The person pushing the wheelchair used to decide when to cross the road. Now I had to do it myself. For a few days I found it difficult to step outside the front door on my own. I forced myself, however, and quickly overcame the hurdle.

For several weeks it felt very strange to walk outside without my stick. Throughout my illness, 'sticky' had gone everywhere with me. While I now never worried that I would need the stick, I felt as if something was missing and would automatically look for it.

During the first few months of being well I did lots of 'new' things. Each time I did something new or went somewhere new I would get nervous. I had been completely dependent on my parents and my confidence had slumped. I had become ill when I was 15 years old and was healed when I was 18. It is during those years that most people start to become more independent but I hadn't. I found I had to do things to boost my confidence, and even very small events like catching a bus on my own seemed difficult at first.

I was also having to think about my future. During my illness I never dared look far ahead. I used to hope I would get well, but it was only a distant thought. Now it had become reality and life stretched ahead of me. In many ways it was brilliant to be able to plan again. Sometimes it seemed rather daunting because the change had been so sudden. I applied to college to take another A-level along with my Sociology. After some thought I decided to make it Music. Most people do three A-levels together, but I decided on two. I didn't want to spend all my time working and have no time to do other things. I had got my life back and was determined to make the most of it. To me, the playing and preparation for church, Junior Church and Shout, and playing and composing for my own pleasure are as important as getting qualifications. I don't want to crowd those things out.

One of the hardest feelings to cope with after I had been healed was the guilt. My first telephone call to Helen, my friend with ME, took a lot of courage to make. When I did phone she was happy about it and we have remained good friends, but I still feel guilty. I have often asked myself, 'Why should *I* be healed?' I am sure there are many people who deserve to be healed much more than I ever did. I don't have an answer. All I can do is accept the gift gratefully and leave the reasoning in God's hands, which is very difficult at times.

Then again, I feel I have betrayed other sufferers. When I was ill, I felt I could identify with them. Now, although I can still empathize with ME sufferers by imagining myself back in their situation, I am not a part of their group any more. Sometimes I feel as if I have abandoned them, and I find it hard to know what to say to someone who has ME who didn't know me when I was ill.

Often I wish I could be a better person to thank God for what He has done for me. I feel as though I ought to be doing more. My own expectations can sometimes be a problem, as can the expectations I feel other people have of me. When I was first healed I was aware of people looking at me, and knew that people said to my friends, 'Isn't that the girl who was in a wheelchair? What's happened to her? She looks so well!'

I was noticed as I walked around because of the sudden change that had taken place. Occasionally, I still feel as if folk might be looking at me, and I often feel some people expect more of me because of what happened. This can be a bit intimidating. I'm 18 years old and I want to be just like anybody else my age.

I do feel different, though. My aim in life is to be happy and healthy. I don't want to be under enormous stress, and money isn't the most important thing. At school great emphasis is put on careers. As long as I am happy and fulfilled I don't mind what I do.

I tend to think of my life in three different phases: before my collapse in 1990, during ME, and after ME. I almost feel as if I have been three people. There is confusion because what happened to me is a miracle and my human brain can't cope with the fact; it is outside my understanding. The time when I had ME can seem like a dream, a nightmare from which I have woken. Sometimes I imagine that I am suffering again and, although I can't feel the physical symptoms any more, the emotions return.

Since I was healed I have had to work through a welter of emotions that I somehow managed to subdue when I was ill. It is as if, though physically healed, the mental and emotional healing is still going on. A while ago I went through a difficult time when the memories of my illness and the associated feelings came back very strongly. I found I couldn't work on this book for a while because it upset me so much, and whenever I saw somebody in a wheelchair it made me want to cry. I underwent counselling, which helped, and the feelings gradually went away. These emotions still recur at times, though. For example, at Christmas 1993, I saw the same Christmas musical I had taken part in only a year before. I didn't think that it might upset me, but that night I came home and cried because it brought back just how low I had felt after I had played my keyboard the year before. I think time will help, however, as I will soon be at the point where 'this time last year' won't overlap into my illness, and I will have new, happier memories to look back on.

As I come to the end of my book, it is the last day of 1993 and almost a year since I was healed. That year has been a very good one for me, so full of change. I have been able to go out with my friends and family to the cinema, bowling, discos, meals out, and walks. In the summer I went on holiday with my friends and had a great time.

In September I started at Sixth Form College to take Music at A-level and to continue with my Sociology. I have made many new friends and particularly enjoy the social aspect of being in school again.

I continue to spend a lot of time playing my keyboard, both at home and in church, and I enjoy composing on both the piano and keyboard. I am not sure exactly what I want to do in the future, but I hope it will involve music.

The events of my illness and healing have had a big

effect on my family too. Overall, what we have been through together has brought us closer. My dad in particular changed much. Soon after I had been healed, I insisted that he tell me what he had experienced that November day which had convinced him that I would get well. He had difficulty talking about it. In fact it took several months before the whole story came out. This is what Dad told me:

On that afternoon he had been feeling distraught and had gone upstairs. He had prayed, imploring God to free me from my illness. He had even prayed that he might have ME instead of me. After this he had been filled with a feeling of complete peace and had known that I would be healed in the new year.

When Dad prayed he wasn't a Christian, although he believed in God. Praying, then, was a big step for him. Since that time Dad has become a committed Christian and now attends church with us regularly.

I can see that God has been working in my life and in the lives of my family, despite all the problems we faced during my illness. I think the most amazing thing is the fact that God cares for everybody in an individual way. As far as the world is concerned I am a 'nobody', yet God has performed a miracle in my life. I don't know what the years to come will hold, but at least I can be confident that God will be there with me.

CHAPTER 16

Through Sue's eyes

September-October 1991.

I was asked by Hazel to share in testimony at another church. During the course of that testimony I expressed my deep concern for Kathryn's healing. The following is an extract from my notes written at the time:

'I believe He is now leading me to search for the gift of healing. It is difficult to know, however, is it not, when we are hearing ourselves and when we are hearing God through His Word or through some other means. I know that when God wants to say something to us He will say it again and again until we hear.

'I have felt for a considerable time a great burden for Kathryn Green and her family. Kathryn is suffering from ME and I know that the people here are experiencing similar feelings for Helen. I believe the Lord is telling me He is going to heal Kathryn and that somehow He wants to involve me. Now that frightens me. The feeling I have is quite like a burden for that family and I continue to wait on the Lord for His leading.'

Following a Sunday service, a lady I didn't know came to me and said, 'I have a word for you from the Lord. You are to step out in faith: just do it.' I can't begin to explain how I felt — it was both uncanny and glorious, that the Lord should speak to me through another person. Then a group of people prayed with me and I suppose that was my commissioning, if you like. I wasn't really aware that it was at the time.

Looking back through my notes, I continue to be amazed by what I said and can't believe I ever said it at all. The fact remains that I did, and I know that I was under total conviction that what I said was true.

Some time after, again in October, I had a phone call from a friend who attends a church a few miles away. She knew of my burden for Kathryn, and her phone call was to tell me I should go and pray with Kathryn. My immediate reaction was, 'I can't.' I couldn't just go up to Kathryn and say, 'I'm going to pray with you.' I felt I had to be invited — so I didn't do anything, only felt extremely guilty.

November 1991 — Willersley weekend.
When Kathryn turned up unexpectedly at Willersley, I thought I had every opportunity to pray with her. Again I held back and put it off.

Sunday 17 January 1993.
Communion Service.
My hand was trembling during the service and I asked the Lord to use me and to show me where and how.

Sunday 24 January.
I led the evening service tonight.
Nora, Kathryn's mum, had asked me if she could talk to me afterwards.
She shared with me the situation in which Kathryn found herself with the offer of a 'healer'. It turned out on further investigation that he was not a Christian healer. He had passed on a message that he could help Kathryn but that it would take about five weeks and he would need to see her every day!
Nora had said that Kathryn was very upset and depressed by it all. It was as if a solution to her illness was within her grasp, but she felt that even so she could not put her trust in that man.
Nora told Hazel about it on Sunday 17th and she said that she was also going to share it with me on the same evening, but because I was upset over our business she hadn't said anything about it.

Because Kathryn had been so very upset, Nora went to Hazel for advice on Friday 22 January and Hazel said she should speak to me and ask me to go and pray with Kathryn regularly every week.

As Nora shared all of it with me, I knew for certain that it was of the Lord and that there was no way I could refuse. I had had a burden for Kathryn for such a long time but had put off actually praying with her (except for one occasion when she had been very poorly and Nora had asked me to go). I knew the Lord was telling me that I should meet with Kathryn for prayer as long ago as November 1991. I was not obedient. I didn't look to Him for strength or leading. I didn't step out in faith as I had been told to. I even called a prayer meeting one Saturday morning to see if I could redeem myself that way. Latterly, I shared in a healing service at which Kathryn was present; and although many blessings were received, it was not the right way forward. I skirted round the problem by trying to find my own solutions!

Thursday 28 January.

Bearing in mind that Nora had referred to how busy I was I felt it was uncanny that my book of daily readings and words of encouragement should say this: 'Fear not. Do not fear to be busy. You are the servant of them all. . . . Be used. Be used by all.'

It was the day I had arranged to meet with Kathryn. As Nora had music pupils at the house until 7.30pm we decided I would aim to call at about 7.45pm.

I had not told anyone of the plans but decided to share what we were doing with a friend from church. I knew she was having similar experiences with the work the Lord had called her to do, and that she would be only too pleased to pray during the time I was with Kathryn. I also knew that Nora had told a mutual friend what was going on, so prayer was also coming from that direction.

When I arrived, Kathryn had not had a very good day and looked very pale and limp. She had visited the dentist on the previous Tuesday and thought that that had added to her feeling poorly.

We neither of us knew quite what form our time together would take. We spent a short time sharing how we felt. Kathryn said that she felt 'tested to the limit' with the thing she most wanted in her life and that she had had to say 'no'. I told her that I knew the Lord wanted me involved with her and the family through this, and of the growing rapport which Nora and I had with each other.

We read together from Ephesians chapter 6 (the armour of God) and committed our time to the Lord.

I have rarely experienced such a profound sense of peace and the presence of God as I did that night. It was a peace that I didn't want to leave and a peace that I could feel; an enfolding peace. This was right. This time we had got it right! We spent about thirty minutes together, that's all. I didn't want to tire Kathryn, and yet at the same time was loath to move away from such peace.

As I drove home the peace of the Lord went with me and I cried.

Sunday 31 January. (Diary)

Nora told me this morning that Kathryn had walked around the block yesterday for the first time since her relapse in March of last year! (A walk which I understand took place at a fair rate of knots.) Needless to say, I was delighted.

At the evening service, before Nora led our prayers of intercession, she told the congregation what we had been doing and then told them what she had told me in the morning. To my utter astonishment, she then added that that afternoon on their walk around the block, Kathryn had handed her her stick, and said she didn't need it any more!

I'm arranging to meet Kathryn again next Thursday 4 February.

Monday 1 February.

Tonight I had a telephone call from Kathryn to tell me how she was. She sounded wonderful! Her voice was stronger than I have ever heard it.

She said that she went to bed last night without taking her tablet, and that she slept for the first time and didn't wake until 5.45am, at which time she was so excited that she couldn't go back to sleep and went to tell her mum. She told me how she had walked around the block without her stick, and that her legs felt so strong. She said they were not at all wobbly. She also told me that she had been able to read again — something which she had not been able to do during her illness owing to her inability to concentrate for any length of time.

I was beside myself by now and had to go to a meeting that night, so asked her if I could ring the Bible-study group so that they would know. Kathryn said that was fine. I rang the leader of the group and asked her to pass the news on for me.

I was also able to share the news with the folk at the meeting, giving them the gist of events, although in a much condensed form owing to the time available.

Tuesday 2 February.

I didn't sleep much last night; my heart and mind were too full of praise!

I phoned Kathryn tonight and she said she was very well. She had been out during the afternoon alone. She said she had also slept well again. She was going to make phone calls to her relatives and friends. My heart is so full for that family! Kathryn then said she was going to see the teachers at school tomorrow — a route that will take her uphill for some distance.

Thursday 4 February.

My day to visit Kathryn. I know she's doing OK but as yet I haven't actually seen her.

As always I consulted my book of Scripture verses and daily thoughts and today's was headed 'Drop your crutch' — 'Just go step by step. My will shall be revealed as you go. . . . When human support or material help is removed, then My power can become operative. I cannot teach a man to walk who is trusting to a crutch. Away with your crutch and My power shall so invigorate you that you shall indeed walk on to victory. Never limit My power. It is limitless.'

Kathryn looks wonderful. It was hugs all round. I took my diary with me to share the verse with them all. I also took my notes from 1991 when I gave my testimony.

Kathryn was keen to go for a walk so we had a stroll around the houses, excitedly sharing how we felt. When we arrived back at the house we spent some time in prayer and thanksgiving, then shared some more with the rest of the family.

Friday 5 February.

Kathryn spent the whole two hours (for the first time) at the Shout group meeting and then went out with the young people.

Saturday 6 February.

Had to ring to check Kathryn was OK. She was. She had finished up at a friend's with a bag of chips and went home about 10.45pm.

Sunday 7 February.

I shared with the congregation what has been happening (again in a slightly condensed fashion) and we were then, as a church, able to give thanks to God for His power and love. Kathryn was able to be in the service (a thing she could not have done before) and the whole family were present. We then went into Junior Church.

Kathryn was present at the service tonight and I felt I needed to share some more when presented with an opportunity. People need to know that prayer brings results, that God is at work among His people!

What has been apparent to me through all this is obedience. Kathryn's obedience to the Lord by denying herself human help through the 'healer' and mine at long last in responding to what the Lord had actually said to me — that I should pray with Kathryn.

It also occurred to me that when I told Nora I would come and pray with Kathryn, I was making a commitment to something which could have lasted for twelve months or more. There was no way of knowing that Kathryn's healing would take place so soon. I believe the Lord honoured all of this.

The Lord has blessed us beyond our imagining through Kathryn's healing and since, but the glory is His alone. Prayer is our way to the Lord. Be very careful what you say to Him. He will hear, so don't be surprised when He answers!

The Minister's Testimony

I moved to Sandiacre Methodist church as the minister in 1988, where I met Philip and Nora Green and their two daughters Kathryn and Alison.

Gradually I got to know the family, becoming friends with Nora. It was obvious that the whole family needed spiritual, physical and mental support. This was given over the years by the loving care of family, friends and the church fellowship.

It was while chatting with Nora one day that I offered to pray with Kathryn, and over a period of time we shared together her hopes and fears. I explained that before complete healing could take place there were some things we must deal with. Bitterness against those who had not understood; bringing before God the people Kathryn needed to forgive, such as teachers and doctors; then there would be the openness to God for Him to work in her life.

Obviously there were days when it seemed healing would not come — days when depression set in — on those days there was only the Lord to rely on.

We heard of a gentleman in Cheshire who was a healer. By the way he was described to me he did not sound as if he was a Christian healer, and I felt that it would be wrong to visit him. Round about this time we discovered that the gift of healing had been given to one of the church members, Sue Grocock. It seemed right that she should come and pray with Kathryn.

She did so, Kathryn was healed, prayers were answered, and new life has been given to that family.

It has been a privilege for me to have met and known Kathryn.

Revd Hazel Humphries

CORNWALL
3 OCTOBER 1994